S0-BDT-363

IN SEARCH OF A WHALE

Marlin Perkins' Wild Kingdom

IN SEARCH OF A WHALE

ALLAN W. ECKERT

With an introduction by Marlin Perkins
Illustrated by Joseph Cellini

Doubleday & Company, Inc., Garden City, New York

LIBRARY OF CONGRESS CATALOG CARD NUMBER 69-15172

PRINTED IN THE UNITED STATES OF AMERICA
FIRST EDITION

Introduction

The sea is a wild kingdom unsurpassed by any other. Beneath its restless surface reside a great multitude of creatures, many of which have not yet even been discovered and scientifically described. Among the submerged valleys and mountains, amid the thick jungles of seaweed and the great plains of marine grasses, within the vast stretches of sandy submerged deserts and jagged coral reefs, along the rocky, rolling, smooth, or cliffed shore lines, there lives an incredible abundance of life. It is life about which we human beings know only a very little. By degrees we are unlocking these secrets, and the capture of living whales has opened a whole new chapter to our understanding of life within the sea.

It is into this marine habitat that "Wild Kingdom" goes now —in search of information and excitement and adventure and, most of all . . . in search of a whale.

Marlin Perkins

Acknowledgments

This book is based on an original story developed for an episode of the internationally known television series, "Wild Kingdom," and I am deeply grateful for the research assistance and continued support graciously given me by the staff of Don Meier Productions, producers of this outstanding program.

The assistance of the personnel in general of Marineland of the Pacific at Palos Verdes, California, is gratefully acknowledged in the research and preparation of this book. Specifically at that institution, sincere gratitude is extended to the crew of the boat *Geronimo*, Frank Brocato, Frank Calandrino, and Benny Falcone, as well as to Marineland president William F. Monahan, vice-president public relations William Campeau, and the institution's curator, John Prescott.

For invaluable information on the life and habits of the pilot whale, we are indebted to Dr. Raymond M. Gilmore, who is presently research associate dealing with marine mammals at the Museum of Natural History, San Diego, California. Dr. Gilmore was formerly research biologist for whale investigations undertaken by the United States Fish and Wildlife Service.

Finally, I wish to thank Don Meier himself for his invaluable creative guidance and generous editing efforts in the expansion of the original story into this full-length zoologically precise book.

ALLAN W. ECKERT

Foreword

If you were asked to make a guess, which would you name as the most difficult mammal in the world to catch alive and then *keep* alive in captivity? There are a great many mammals in the world from which to choose—thirty-five hundred known species which are further broken down to about fifteen thousand sub-species. Some of these are fierce and very dangerous creatures;

others have mild or even timid dispositions. And most of these species are today represented by living individuals in one or more zoos around the world.

Your first thought in answer to the question asked above was very probably a member of the cat family—lion, tiger, leopard, or jaguar—because of the fierceness of those creatures. Yet few reputable zoos in the world do not have one or more of them.

Perhaps you might have selected as your guess one of the larger mammals, particularly those of Africa—the elephant or rhinoceros, the water buffalo or the hippopotamus, or even the gangly giraffe. Maybe you thought it would be one of the bears—grizzly or polar, Siberian or Alaska brown, or others of that family.

Or, having given it a little more thought, you might even have picked one of the rarer mammals, such as the Tasmanian devil, the duckbill platypus, the giant panda, or the okapi.

Yet the answer is none of these.

For dozens or scores or even hundreds of years the majority of those creatures named above have been sought, trapped, and brought back alive to zoos all over the world; not only for visitors to see and marvel at them, but for scientists to study them in depth so that we may know more about the world in which we live and the creatures which inhabit it.

Zoos are not a development of the modern world, though many of us tend to think of them as such. As far back as the great Chinese dynasties, the Khans had large animal compounds or gardens. The ancient Egyptians, too, had their unusual animal collections, normally in the possession of a princess or pharaoh. Later still, the Greeks and Romans had their share of zoos. So zoos are not at all a new item, though over the centuries they have improved considerably.

Yet, over these years there has been one group of creatures —mammals, and not really so rare at that—which somehow managed to keep itself free of captivity. This was the whale family.

Many were killed, of course. Throughout the centuries thousands of them have been harpooned and a whole industry was built around seeking them out and killing them, mostly for the valuable oils which could be rendered from their thick blubber and out of their heads. But as far as actually catching one alive was concerned, bringing it back alive, and then *keeping* it alive in safety and comfort, it was generally believed that this was impossible, or at least highly improbable.

But then the picture suddenly changed. A small group of men in southern California became convinced that somehow it must be possible to do this and for months they tried . . . unsuccessfully. It was an entirely new field of endeavor and there were staggering problems to contend with. In a wild kingdom as broad and deep and unexplored as the sea, how could one hope to capture so large and intelligent a creature? And even if caught, how could it possibly be kept alive?

One by one a wide variety of methods were tried and discarded as they were found to be unsuitable or impractical. And then finally, as recently as 1957, these men actually sought, caught, and brought back to captivity a living whale; a pilot whale which they named Bubbles and which still lives in perfect contentment in captivity today, a decade later.

Since that time these men have caught a number of whales which have been brought back alive to Marineland of the Pacific. These captive whales are, quite naturally, a great attraction. Amazingly intelligent, they quickly adapt to their new surroundings and learn, on command of a trainer, to jump, dance in the water, and perform a wide variety of stunts. They are immensely popular creatures and, as a result, literally millions of people have come to the institution to see them.

But entertainment value is far from the only reason these whales are captured alive. Although man has learned a great deal about most of the land mammals on earth, he knows comparatively little about the lives and habits of marine mammals, the whales in particular. These men, in catching and bringing back alive whale specimens such as these, have provided experts in marine mammalogy their first opportunity to study these cetaceans in depth, observing them and testing them over long periods of time.

Such research has paid off handsomely. Only a decade ago man's total knowledge about whales had come only from observations on the sea and in examining the remains of whales that had been harpooned or else whales that had become marooned in shallow waters and died. Now, however, largely through the daily research being carried out at the Marineland of the Pacific oceanarium, man has begun to understand much better the nature, habits, and life cycle of the whale.

MARINELAND OF THE PACIFIC

Chapter One

It was in its narrow slip in Los Angeles Harbor at San Pedro, California, that Marlin Perkins of "Wild Kingdom" caught his first glimpse of the boat named *Geronimo*. This was the craft which was to take him out to sea in search of a whale. He could not help thinking that it seemed to be a rather small boat for such a big job.

Relatively small it might have been, but the *Geronimo* was particularly well-manned and well-equipped for such an extensive and potentially dangerous mission. From bow to stern it measured only thirty-eight feet and its beam—that distance from side to side across the deck at the widest part—was twelve feet. A sixteen-foot mast sticking sturdily upward from amidships supported the radio antenna, and a thick, smooth crossboard near the top served as a makeshift crow's-nest lookout perch. Two quickly narrowing ladders made of cables and wood provided access to this lookout crossboard from the rail on either side of the boat.

The most immediately obvious difference in the boat, however,

was an uncommonly long and rather peculiar bowsprit that projected far ahead of the prow. Firmly anchored by cables to mast, cabin and both port and starboard bow rails, it was a sturdy board construction stretching twenty-six feet ahead of the boat. At its end was an iron framework basket built to hold a man. Very soon now, Marlin knew, he himself would be standing in that contraption, perhaps looking down at a whale only five or six feet directly beneath him.

Tied up in its slip, here in the quiet waters of the harbor, the bowsprit basket did not look to be an especially dangerous place to ride. Nor did it appear that it would be much of a trick to walk that narrow planking out to the basket. After all, the walkway was six inches wide and nearly three inches thick, the cables provided fairly substantial handholds, and it looked as if it would be a snap getting out there.

Marlin Perkins wasn't fooled by the seeming easiness of it. When this relatively small craft was far out at sea with great waves breaking the surface and tremendous swells causing the boat to nose far up or down or tilt dangerously from side to side, it would be almost impossible to hold one's balance on the main deck, let alone on this narrow strip of planking which would then be slick with sea water. Yet it was something that would have to be done.

On board were three men moving about the deck purposefully. At the moment they were engaged in stowing gear and supplies. It was plain to see they meant to be well prepared for this forthcoming expedition. A wide variety of fresh fruits, vegetables, baked goods, meats, and staple items were being stowed away in proper watertight compartments; those requiring refrigeration being placed beside or atop great blocks of ice in a large thermal ice chest. Rainwear and ropes, nets, long aluminum poles, tarpaulins, sheets, canvas, and a considerable collection of other gear were being carefully put away. The job, in fact, was nearly completed as Marlin Perkins walked out on the dock, greeted the men, and was enthusiastically welcomed aboard.

These three were the entire crew of the *Geronimo*; strong,

tough, experienced men who had spent their lifetimes on the sea and are as familiar with the Pacific coastal waters from the southern tip of Baja California, to British Columbia, Canada, as most of us are with the street upon which we live.

Captain Frank Brocato is the senior member of the crew. A short, chunky man of sixty-two, his body as solid as an oaken barrel, he can perform with ease tasks requiring enormous strength and dexterity; tasks which would quickly leave many a landlubber weak and gasping.

For some years Captain Brocato had been skipper of the *Geronimo*. In mid-1967, however, he had been elevated to a vice presidency in the Marineland of the Pacific corporation and his title aboard the boat—though he is still the authority aboard—is Director of Collections. It is a title well deserved.

The actual skipper of the *Geronimo* now is Captain Frank Calandrino, better known to one and all by the nickname of "Boots." Brocato and Calandrino's father were the very best of friends and, when the latter died while Boots was still a small boy, Brocato immediately took Boots under his wing. Even as a youngster of seven or eight, Boots was working about ship under Brocato, scrambling about in high rubber boots six or eight sizes too large, which was something of a ludicrous sight. From this stemmed the nickname.

Now, at age forty-two, Boots has taken Brocato's place as skipper of the *Geronimo* and he is very well qualified for the responsibility. A lifetime of living with the sea has filled him with an incredible knowledge of it and deep respect for it. To him, the sea is a personality; a fickle woman who aids the seafarer when treated with respect but who, when taken for granted or scoffed at, destroys in fits of savage anger before which no craft can stand.

Third member of the team is fifty-nine-year-old Benny Falcone. He is a quiet, friendly individual, tall and lean, who has spent his lifetime on the sea engaged in a variety of occupations: skipper, commercial fisherman, fishing guide, collector, and related activities. A staunch, dependable man, Benny works himself as neither

Frank nor Boots would think of working him. Without having to be told, he knows precisely what to do and when to do it and he is an extremely good man to have around in an emergency. Though slightly built, the muscles of his arms and legs, back and shoulders are like cables lying beneath the skin.

All three crew members share a prime essential; an eyesight little short of phenomenal. From a distance of two miles or more they can spot a whale or shark or dolphin breaking the surface and not only correctly identify it, but accurately estimate its size and what it is doing in the area. Such ability is extremely important in this business of hunting the whale.

Already, in these few minutes he has been on board the *Geronimo*, Marlin Perkins is impressed with the ability of this crew, their lack of wasted effort, their complete control over what they are engaged in at any given moment. There is no doubt in his mind that these are highly skilled, professional men, and he feels secure in the knowledge that they are to be at his side.

It is a good feeling to have when one heads out into the wild kingdom of the sea.

Although he has shared in the capture of wild animals around the world, seeking the whale is a new experience for Marlin and he is eager for the journey to begin.

This present expedition is a joint endeavor of the personnel of Marineland of the Pacific and the producers of the "Wild Kingdom" television series in which the exploits and adventures of Marlin Perkins have been followed around the globe. For Marineland, it is an opportunity to add yet another cetacean—a pilot whale—to their growing collection. For Marlin it is an opportunity to penetrate another wild kingdom and experience another grand adventure. For both parties it is an opportunity, possibly, to unlock more secrets of nature and enable man to understand his world all the better.

There was hope that on this expedition they might be able to capture alive a good-sized blue shark and possibly a nice sea lion as well. But most important, it was a search for a whale, hopefully an adult pilot whale seventeen or eighteen feet in length but, if not an adult, then at least a young animal of perhaps half that size.

Each of the men knew only too well that the odds were strongly stacked against them.

Chapter Two

For Frank Brocato, Boots Calandrino, and Benny Falcone, the expedition they were setting off on now was simply another of many similar expeditions they had shared. For Marlin Perkins, however, it was entirely new and the thought of actually catching a pilot whale alive was most exciting.

As the crew made their final preparations for casting off, Marlin reviewed briefly some of the facts he already knew about their quarry.

The pilot whale is also known as the pothead whale, the caa'ing whale, and the blackfish. There is good reason behind each of the names. The term "pilot" comes from the fact that when harpooned by a hunter or badly frightened, the leader of the whale herd—or pod, as a school of whales is called—will "pilot" the rest of the whales into shallow water and death at the hands of the whalers or the elements.

On the northeast coast of the United States, it is known as the pothead because the shiny black head, especially on adult males, seems swollen like a great black pot. This very feature, Marlin recalled, is also responsible for the Latin name of the species, which is *Globicephala*, meaning "ball-headed."

The name caa'ing whale is not clear in its origin. Possibly it came about because of the bellowing sound (or caa'ing, as the Scots call it) made by beached whales driven ashore by hunters. Finally, it is called blackfish because of its general color, though this is a poor name because, of course, the whale is a mammal, not a fish.

Found in various oceans of the world, except those of polar regions, there are several subspecies of the pilot whale, but in these California waters the quarry of the men on the *Geronimo* would be the one known as *Globicephala scammoni*, which is found in the Pacific coastal waters from the Gulf of Alaska south to Guatemala.

Where whales are concerned, the pilot is not an especially large species. At the Newfoundland whalery, where Canadian biologists have measured many thousands of them, the maximum length for the bulls was twenty feet. For cows, it was seventeen feet. Stories have been told of pilot whales which were supposedly twenty-eight or thirty feet in length, but no such size has ever been authenticated.

Marlin abruptly broke off his train of thought to watch with interest as one final job was completed by the crew. Using the *Geronimo*'s winch and boom, they were lifting from the dock into the boat a large steel framework cage just big enough to hold a man standing up.

It was an important item, for in this cage Marlin would be lowered beneath the surface to take pictures of some of the most dangerous creatures imaginable—great blue sharks whose fantastic teeth and jaws have the power to sever a man's limbs and tear him to pieces in a matter of minutes.

Marlin walked over to the cage on deck and felt the half inch bars and nodded. The device seemed very strong, well-built, and wellnigh impregnable here aboard the *Geronimo* but when surrounded by blood-maddened sharks butting it with their power-

ful snouts, it could be another matter entirely. "We'll soon know one way or another," Marlin thought.

Now, with everything aboard and stowed, it was time for the expedition to begin. If luck rode with them, it was altogether possible that they might be able to find their whale, catch it, and bring it back to the oceanarium all in a day's time. But, even though it has happened in the past, none of the four men had any real confidence that it would happen this time.

As Benny undid the reefing ropes and Brocato climbed to the control seat on the upper deck, Boots stood beside Marlin and they talked about it.

"There was one time several years ago," Boots said, "when we left the harbor here at San Pedro, followed the coast line up toward Marineland and on the way, only a few miles out, we encountered a pod of pilot whales. On the very first try we caught one, got it in all right, and within an hour or so it was swimming around in one of the oceanarium tanks. That," he added with a grin, "rarely happens."

They were words Marlin had a peculiar feeling he would remember later, especially when Captain Brocato turned around in his seat and said, "There've also been times when we searched for a week or more without even *seeing* a pod, much less catching one of the whales. And even if we do spot some pods fairly soon, the chance of catching an individual from them are pretty slim. I just wouldn't want you to be too disappointed if we come back empty-handed."

With that he started the motor and immediately a deep powerful throbbing came from below decks. While graceful herring gulls wheeled low overhead, looking for a handout, the *Geronimo* backed out of its slip with a smoothness belying its squat, bulky shape. As if it had eyes of its own, the boat turned easily in a space where clearance between it and other moored boats was only scant feet and then moved powerfully forward toward the distant opening in the long curving rock jetty which guarded the harbor.

Marlin climbed the rigging to the upper deck and sat near Brocato as they moved at quarter-throttle toward the open sea.

While Boots and Benny busied themselves below, the pair above talked of oceanaria and their importance, not only as a source of interest and entertainment for the visiting public, but equally as marine research centers where facts about the world beneath the sea are constantly being discovered.

Marineland of the Pacific was not the first oceanarium in the United States, but there can be no doubt that it is the largest and most important in the world today. The first was Marineland of Florida, which was built at St. Augustine in 1938. Sixteen years later, in 1954, Marineland of the Pacific was opened to the public, located on the southwestern tip of Palos Verdes Peninsula about twenty-five miles south of downtown Los Angeles. Other oceanaria were soon constructed elsewhere—the Seaquarium in Miami was built the following year and, in 1964, the Sea World was opened near San Diego. Hawaii has one as well now, and there are smaller oceanaria at Sarasota, Florida, in Tokyo, Japan, at Durban, South Africa, and in Queensland, Australia.

It was the construction of gigantic concrete tanks capable of holding hundreds of thousands of gallons of sea water which, after so many years of whale harpooning, permitted whales to be taken alive and brought back to live in captivity. And it was Captain Frank Brocato who became the first man in the world to hunt, capture, and bring back a living whale.

"I'll have to admit," Brocato told Marlin now, "that it really wasn't the first whale in captivity. Back on October 6, 1948, there was a pod of pilot whales—forty-six of 'em—which for some unknown reason deliberately swam ashore and beached themselves in Florida."

Pilot whales are strange that way, Marlin knew. Time and again over the years they have beached themselves and seem intent upon committing mass suicide. These pods are normally led by one large individual, usually a bull. The pod itself may number from as few as a half dozen or so whales to as many as hundreds or even a few thousand. Marlin recalled that once a pod of three thousand of the mammals had been reported.

Such pods will follow their leader with dogged persistence wherever he pilots them. Should something frighten him and cause him to speed into the shallows—perhaps the sight of a pack of killer whales or some equally distressing danger—the entire pod will follow and become beached along with him. There have been times when whales which beached themselves in this way were pulled by boats to deeper water again, only to swim right back in and beach themselves again as soon as they were released.

There are records of such mass strandings all over the world. At Cape Cod, Massachusetts, alone, there have been recorded strandings of 1,400, 768, and 741 individuals, for a total of 2,909 whales in just three stranded pods. At the Faeroe Islands, not far from Iceland, there have been strandings of 657, 600, 450, and 250. Once in Norway, 1,000 were stranded at once.

Marlin was aware that such strandings are popularly called mass suicide, but he shook his head at that. It wasn't a good term to use. By definition, suicide is performed with a wish for death and Marlin knew it was most unlikely that any animal besides man can anticipate death and successfully and deliberately destroy himself with that goal in mind.

But this was getting off the track of their conversation and Marlin returned his attention to Captain Brocato.

"Anyway," the older seaman said, "when that pod of pilots beached themselves in Florida in 1948, they couldn't be saved, even though attempts were made to help them. One of them was a nice young male still very much alive, so he was lifted into a truck and taken to Florida's Marine Studios. They named him Herman and put him in their dolphin tank, which was the only place they had big enough to hold him.

"He was about seven and a half feet long and maybe three hundred pounds; probably no more than five or six months old. But in August of '49, the male bottlenose dolphins—*Tursiops*—in the tank went into their mating period and it seems they resented the presence of the whale there. Several of them attacked and killed him. Too late, the personnel there realized that *Tursiops* and whales, small ones at least, should not be penned together."

A note of pride entered Frank Brocato's voice as he continued. "Ours was the first whale, though, that was actually captured out in the ocean—the first time anyone had deliberately gone out with the goal of catching one alive and really doing it. That was on February 27, 1957."

This was Marineland's famous whale, Bubbles, that Captain Brocato was speaking of—a pilot whale that was an estimated twelve feet in length at time of capture and weighed about twelve hundred pounds. "She was probably about six years old," Brocato added, "and she's grown a lot since then. Just seventeen months after we brought her in we had to move her to another tank and that gave us a chance to weigh and measure her again. By then she was nearly a foot longer and had put on about a hundred pounds. Last time we measured her, in March of '60, she was exactly thirteen feet eleven inches long and weighed thirteen hundred and sixty pounds. She's a lot bigger than that now.

"Even in the capture of Bubbles," Brocato said, "we learned something about whale behavior. We took her off Santa Catalina Island—in the area we're heading for right now—where she was part of a pod of about twenty-five whales.

"We managed to throw a noose around her but had a tough time getting her in. The other whales seemed to be working almost in teams to try to knock the rope off her. Took us better than an hour to get her alongside the boat and she was too big to bring aboard, so we put our big long rubber raft under her, inflated it, and then towed her all the way back in that.

"Do you know," he told Marlin, "that entire pod of whales followed us all the way back to the coast and kept milling all around us, even when we were raising her to the truck with the dock crane. Quite a sight."

Since that capture of Bubbles, the crew of the *Geronimo* have captured a number of other whales. Squirt, a four-year-old female weighing a thousand pounds and ten feet four inches long was caught on June 19, 1957, and their first male, the famous Bimbo, was taken on January 21, 1959. He was seventeen feet three inches then and weighed about three thousand pounds. In June, 1967, Bimbo was close to double that weight and approaching twenty-one feet in length, which is decidedly a record for the species.

Other teams of men along the West Coast and elsewhere have tried to duplicate the feats of the crew of the *Geronimo* but, thus far at any rate, they have fallen far short. An occasional very small whale has been taken, but none anywhere near the size of those taken by the *Geronimo* and no one else has even approached her record in numbers taken.

Despite the fact that they have now caught quite a few whales, the great excitement and sense of adventure accompanying each expedition has never diminished for the crew of the *Geronimo*. Theirs was a form of adventure few men ever have the opportunity to share and one that now, more than ever, Marlin Perkins was looking forward to.

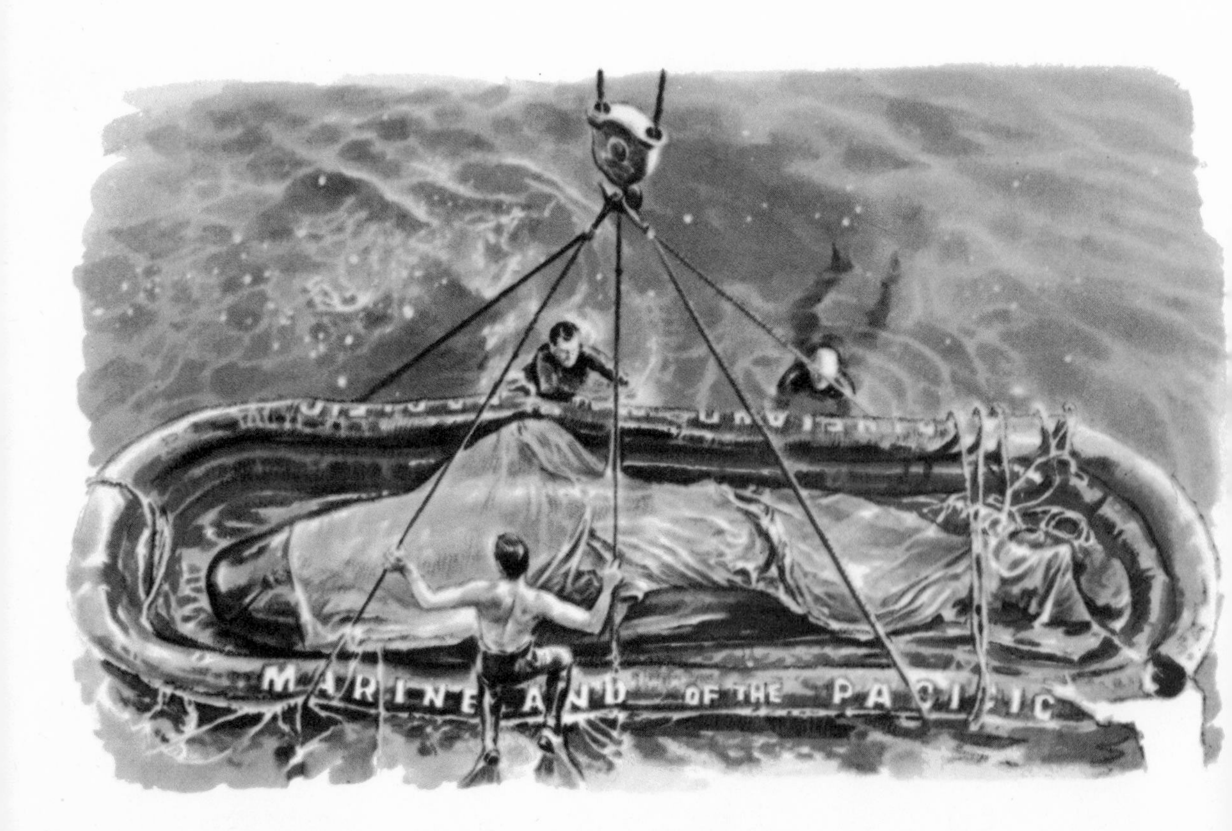

Chapter Three

Immediately after pulling out of Los Angeles Harbor and entering the sea proper, there was a distinct change noticed by Marlin in the character of the water. It became a deep blue-green, indicative of very deep waters, and lost much of the inshore murkiness. And now, even though there was practically no breeze and the water surface was barely rippled, great heaving swells caused the *Geronimo* to rise and fall as much as ten or twelve feet.

The sky was uniformly overcast and Marlin wondered about heading far out to sea when it appeared there might be a bad storm in prospect. He asked Boots about it and the skipper flashed the quick bright grin which is his trademark.

"Weather's perfect for us," he said. "If it was bright and sunny this time of the morning, that's when we'd think twice about heading out. Sun in the morning at this time of year means wind, and when the wind kicks up the sea between here and Santa Catalina Island, it can get unbelievably rough. No, the overcast is good. It's normal weather. It'll stay this way most of the day, too. Along about one or two o'clock the overcast will burn off for a few hours. Then it'll close in again."

He shook his head and added, "Hundreds of boats—and people!—are lost every year in these waters because they read the weather wrong. They think because it's clear and bright, it'll be a good day. Far as rain is concerned, maybe that's true, but out here it's the water you have to worry about. Clear weather'll bring waves that can swamp a boat much bigger than this one. More than once we've planned to go back to the coast after hunting and then spent the night anchored at Catalina instead because the skies cleared and the sea got rough. Might not be good for photography to have it overcast like this, but it's best for safety."

There was a marked increase in the large, hoarsely voiced herring gulls around the boat. The white of their bellies and wing undersides flashed brightly against the dark sky, but when they turned so that the gray-blue of their backs and wingtops showed, they became difficult to see.

Here and there lone cormorants and American mergansers rested on the surface, or in little clusters of two or three or four rode the swells easily. Occasionally when the *Geronimo* approached them they submerged, but more often they took to

wing, flapping laboriously along the surface a long way before finally clearing the water and skimming over the swells by a scant few inches until lost from sight.

Visible in all directions on the flat swelling surface were large patches of disturbed water. It looked almost as if rain was falling on these spots. They ranged in size from a dozen yards across to actual acres in area and occasionally from them would come a frantic eruption of the surface which would cease as quickly as it had begun.

Marlin Perkins had no need to ask what these odd patches indicated. He had seen them many times before. They were schools of thousands and even tens of thousands of anchovies. The little fish were swimming just a fraction of an inch beneath the surface, now and then raising their heads above water in curious fashion for just an instant before submerging once again. And it was clear to Marlin, too, what it was that occasionally caused them to sprint so frantically out of the water with a prolonged splashing which sounded like hail falling.

"Bonito feeding on them, eh Benny?"

The lean deck hand nodded. "Probably. Might be a few barracuda around, too. More likely bonito. Lots of 'em close in lately."

Boots joined them and swept his arm out in a gesture which took in the dozen or so sport fishing boats visible around them. "That's what they're after," he said. "Bonito's a good fighter and lots of fun on rod and reel. Not much good on the table, though. Pretty oily meat. Still," he admitted, shrugging, "lots of people eat them and like them."

The bulk of the high-cliffed Palos Verdes Peninsula was now barely visible behind them, gradually being swallowed up in the haze of smog and cloudy overcast which hung in the atmosphere. They were headed, Brocato had told Marlin, for the close-in waters of Santa Catalina Island first. It was there, he said, that they were most apt to spot some whales—provided they saw any at all today.

"Actually," Captain Brocato said, "this isn't the best time of the year to find the whales. They're somewhat migratory in their habits and during December, January, and February these waters right here are often thick with them. I've seen as many as a thousand or more in a day between the coast and Catalina. In early summer like this, though, they tend to move out. Sometimes they'll be around Catalina, which is only twenty-five miles

out, but often they'll go out maybe a hundred or two hundred miles. Hard to say for sure when—or if—we'll find them. We'll give it a good try, though."

Marlin was scanning the sea ahead intently, watching for the bulk of Santa Catalina Island to begin looming, when suddenly he caught sight of a dark shape in the water far ahead.

"There!" he called, pointing to it, and at once three other pairs of eyes locked on the object. Marlin couldn't quite make it out, but they promptly identified it.

"Sea lion," said Boots.

"Dead," said Brocato.

"Probably shot," said Benny Falcone.

As they came nearer and Brocato throttled down a bit, Marlin could see that it was, indeed, a California sea lion, and quite a large one at that; obviously well over a thousand pounds. It was stretched out on its back in the water and its flesh was discolored. The body was beginning to bloat and it was evident that the animal had been dead a considerable while.

"The skin'll probably rupture pretty soon from the pressure of the gasses and then it'll sink," Benny said. "I can't see any bullet hole, but if there is one it's probably on top of the head or neck and out of sight from us, the way it's floating."

Marlin was puzzled. "Who would shoot it like that?" he asked.

Benny shrugged. "Commercial fishermen sometimes. Sports fishermen sometimes. Hard to say. The commercial boys don't like 'em. They get into their nets and tear 'em up pretty bad. They get all tangled up and eventually drown, but they'll ruin a lot of netting before they do. Some of the commercial fishermen'll shoot 'em on sight," he added, a bit defensively, since he himself had once been one of them. "At least they've got something of a reason, which is more than these so-called sportsmen have who carry rifles aboard and shoot anything they see swimming."

Marlin nodded. It is a perpetual hazard which many forms of coastal wildlife face and one which laws are mainly ineffective in controlling. In Florida, for example, the same thing is happening to the manatee, or sea cow, despite the fact that its numbers are now so low that the species is teetering on the brink of extinction. It is not a pleasant thought to realize that some fool in a boat might, for no other reason that "amusement," shoot and kill the last of a species of large and inoffensive mammal. Yet, such a possibility is very real.

He smiled faintly at the defensiveness exhibited by Benny in regard to the commercial fishermen. It was the same story everywhere; there was little love lost between commercial fishermen and game fishermen. Still, he could not condone the shooting of these fine mammals—by anyone. As usual, however, the problem boiled down to one of economics. Where it meant that money might be lost because of a form of wildlife, that creature, whatever it was, immediately found itself in jeopardy.

The dead sea lion was lost in the distance behind and as the *Geronimo* surged ahead at full throttle, Marlin settled back again to watch for whales. Having thoroughly refamiliarized himself with the physical appearance of the species the day before in the Marineland tanks, he was sure he could accurately detect one if it showed itself.

It had been most interesting watching the pilot whales swimming about in those gigantic enclosures. One of these tanks, which was the largest sea tank in the world, contained six hundred forty thousand gallons of water, which was plenty of room for a whale to swim about. There was even room for the animal to breach—that is, to jump out of the water and then splash back in hitting the water with the entire length of its body.

These pilot whales are long and relatively narrow creatures, with a body shape similar to that of an overgrown porpoise. Their heads are bulgy and their mouths are curved with a perpetual grin. Widely separated teeth, sharp but rather peglike, can be seen when they open their mouths.

The tail fin, or flukes, of the pilot whale is surprisingly small and the rear of the body, just in front of the flukes, is very narrow and keeled above and below, especially in the larger bull. Not only does that aid in balance but it makes for less water resistance in the up-and-down motion of the tail while swimming, resulting in greater speed. When turned sideways, the tail acts as a rudder as well as a means of propulsion. The flukes are triangular in shape and, except in the middle between the two segments, have no bones.

The side fins or, more properly, pectoral flippers are curved sharply, like the great scimitars wielded by Mideastern warriors of old. These flippers are located far to the front of the whale's body, where they can control direction just as the front wheels of a car do, except that the flippers move up and down rather than from side to side. Actually, they represent front legs and have bones almost identical in function and position to the arm of a human being.

The crew had told Marlin that probably the portion most likely to be seen first in the distance would be the top—dorsal—fin. In some respects it is like that of a shark or dolphin, but not so sharply pointed as theirs. Not only is it a more rounded fin, but it is also a good bit larger than that of either shark or dolphin. This upper fin is closer to the head than to the tail, which gives the

whale a forward center of gravity. The resultant long rear end of the body, therefore, is able to provide greater leverage for the flukes, greater speed, and greater maneuverability.

The animal's waste vent is on the underside about half way between fluke and dorsal fin and, except when deliberately opened by the whale, is tightly sealed against the water. The air vent—commonly called the blow-hole, which is also kept sealed when submerged, is located on top of the head at the back of the bulge. When opened, it is a hole about the diameter of a teacup.

The color of the whale varies from deep slate gray to distinct ebony black, except for a line of white which begins under the jaw and extends back to end in a heart-shaped patch about midway between the flippers. There is also a somewhat lighter area shaped like a saddle just behind the dorsal fin, though this is considerably more visible when the mammal is underwater than above the surface. There is also a rather grayish area around the vent on the underside. The young ones, Marlin had been informed, are usually considerably lighter than the adults.

The male pilot whale in particular has a great globelike forehead protuberance which is important as a mechanism of both defense and offense. It is a melon of defense fat which grows faster than the body so that it overhangs the jaws and protects them when fighting or ramming. It is also somewhat buoyant and helps to hold the animal's head abovewater during sleep. With this great bulge of fat the whale can ram an enemy, such as a large shark or killer whale, with devastating force; with no injury to self and yet extremely damaging to whatever is struck. One solid blow by that head to the side of a killer whale or other enemy could rupture internal organs and permanently injure or even kill the foe.

The throbbing of the motor and gentle roll of the boat over the swells was pleasant and the air here far out on the sea smelled sweet and fresh. Frank Brocato glanced at his watch and saw that it was already nearing ten o'clock.

"Well, we won't be able to take any big ones today," he commented.

"Why is that?" asked Marlin.

"Anything over eleven or twelve feet gets too big to be lifted on board with the winch. If we get a big one, we have to tow it behind us inside a big inflatable raft which we position beneath it and then inflate. But with such a weight being pulled along behind the boat, we can't make more than four knots.

"Later in the afternoon, just about every day, the sea gets pretty choppy between Catalina and the coast. So much so, in fact, that you just can't maneuver properly while towing. At best we'd lose the whale and at worst we could be capsized by the rough water. So, after about ten o'clock in the morning, we have to settle for a small one, maybe nine or ten feet long."

He pointed to the heavy wooden skiff on the back deck of the boat. Inside it was a large canvas stretcher rigged with rope which could attach to the winch and boom which were a part of the central mast. The ropes attached to heavy pipes which made up the sides of the stretcher.

"With a small one," Brocato explained, "we can get him alongside, lower the stretcher and get it positioned under him and then lift him aboard. We place a mattress and some foam-rubber chunks under him so his own weight won't crush his flippers or otherwise injure him and then go in with him on deck like that. Of course, we have to keep him covered and wetted down, as his skin is very susceptible to drying out and getting sunburned. But being out of water for long stretches doesn't hurt them too much. We've had some of them out for upward of eighteen hours without damage to the whale. Let's hope on this trip we'll be able to show you what I mean."

He smiled slowly. "Keep a good lookout now, Marlin. We could begin to see some pods before long."

Chapter Four

While the crew of the *Geronimo*, in their years of whale hunting, have mostly concentrated on pilot whales, they haven't limited themselves entirely to them. In fact, Frank Brocato and Boots Calandrino share the distinction of being the first men to catch a killer whale alive. The exciting event took place along the Pacific Coast far to the north of California in 1961. At that time the pair lassoed a fourteen-foot killer whale and, in the process, came close to losing their own lives.

The mate of the whale which was roped attacked the boat savagely, ramming it with its head, biting at the hull with its fantastic teeth and slamming it with heavy, shuddering blows of tail and body. Instead of diminishing, the attack grew more severe and suddenly there was a very real danger of the whale sinking the craft. It therefore became necessary for them to shoot the larger whale.

"I don't believe any creature alive has more deadly teeth than the killer whale," Brocato told Marlin now. "They're close to-

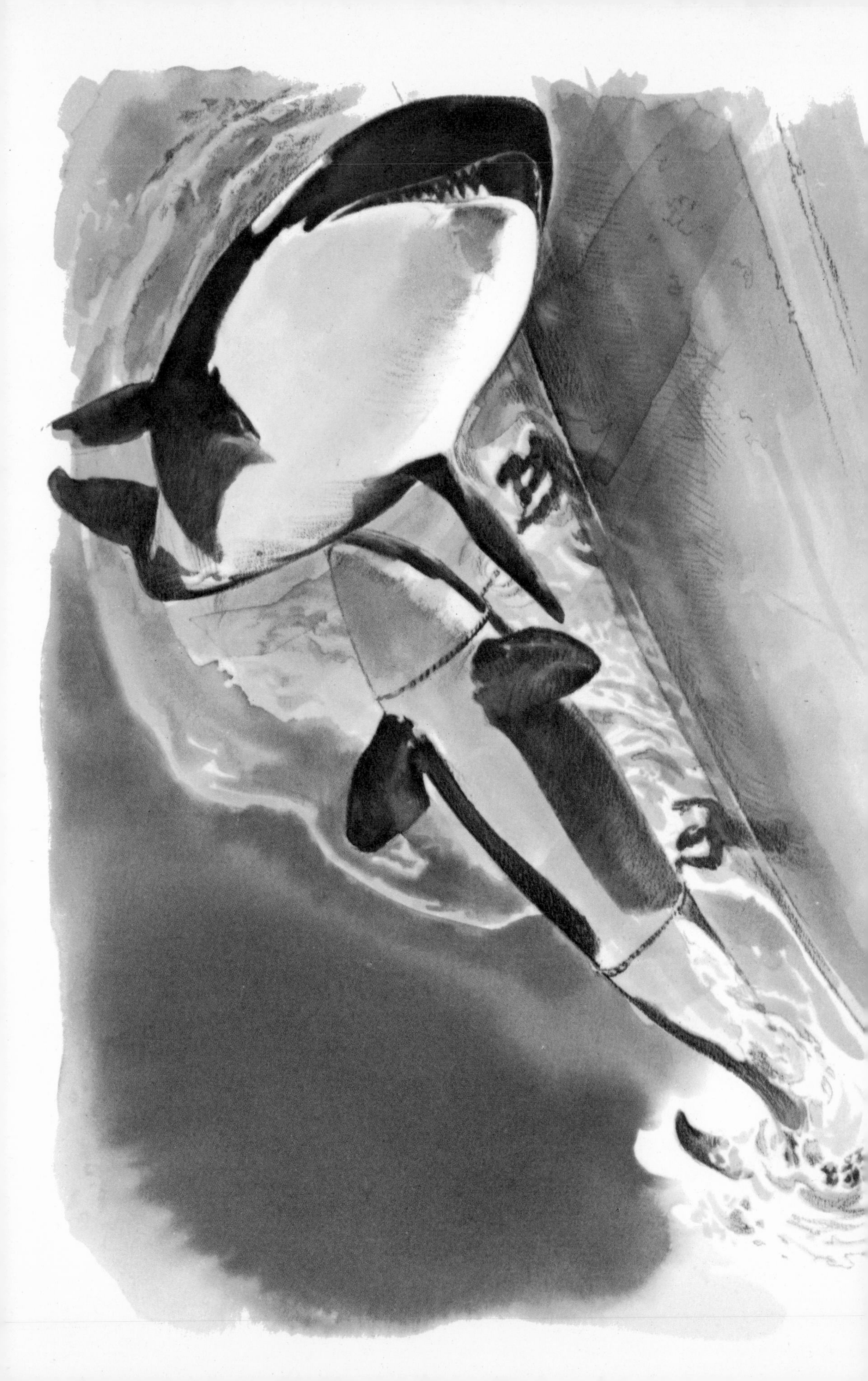

gether, cone-shaped, and very large and strong. Not only that, but when they bite, their upper and lower teeth mesh perfectly, like the teeth of a gear wheel. They can cut a full grown dolphin or seal in half with a single bite."

Brocato shook his head. "Later we wished we hadn't caught it at all. We took it back to shore but right from the beginning it was obvious that something was wrong with it. It became progressively weaker and in eighty hours it just rolled over and died. When we opened it up, we found there was nothing in its stomach."

Marlin raised his eyebrows at that. The killer whale must really have been sick; such whales rarely have empty stomachs. They are voracious eaters and the stomach contents of most of those that have been harpooned have been little short of incredible. There is not much in the sea, if anything, that the killer whale fears. It travels in packs and in close formation, rising and diving in unison. The approach of such a pack can so terrify other marine life that fish will flee at top speed, seals will swim desperately to shore and scramble out of the water, and pilot whales will deliberately beach themselves in an effort to get away, often dying in the shallows when stranded by a lowering tide.

A pack of killer whales might not dare to attack a full grown sperm whale or blue whale, but it is recorded fact that they will unhesitatingly attack other great whalebone whales. They will circle the larger animal as wolves circle a moose or caribou, darting in to bite and otherwise harass it until the larger creature becomes weak. Then they will tear at its lips and tongue until it bleeds to death, whereupon they will cut it to pieces.

Killer whales will eat almost anything but are particularly fond of walrus, porpoise, seals, and small whales—especially pilot whales. Some idea of what a tremendous appetite they have can be seen from the fact that one harpooned killer whale had in his stomach a total of fourteen seals and thirteen porpoises!

The men discussed killer whales for a while longer and it was obvious that Brocato was both proud and delighted with the fact that Marineland only recently—in July 1967—became the home of a fine healthy specimen of killer whale. After a while they began to discuss other species of whales the men have caught.

"Three years after taking that first killer whale," Captain Brocato told Marlin, "we caught the first false killer whale ever taken alive. In fact we caught her not very far from this exact spot. That time though, we had better luck than with that first killer whale. We managed to get her in and back to Marineland safely and she has adapted herself quite well to life there. As a matter of fact, she's learned a number of difficult tricks and has become one of the most popular animals we have. She goes by the name of Swifty now."

The false killer whale—or little killer whale—as Marlin knew, was nothing like his namesake in ferocity. Though they are somewhat similar in shape, the false killer whales do not grow so large and are mild mannered. Average size is only a bit over sixteen feet, with extra large ones going to eighteen feet. Their dorsal fin is much smaller than that of the killer whale and their teeth are nowhere nearly so terrible. Unlike the killer whale, it does not eat large creatures, confining itself almost entirely to squid, cuttlefish, and such fishes as small tuna and bonito.

For another half hour or so the men chatted but then finally lapsed into silence. All of them were watching the water surface closely, their heads swiveling back and forth ceaselessly.

Then, once again it was Marlin who first spotted something in the water ahead. At first he thought it was a seal, for only a small portion of the head was out of the water. As they came closer, however, they saw that it was not a seal after all but, rather, a baby sea elephant—also called elephant seal.

"By golly," Brocato said, "look there, Boots. We don't see many that small."

Boots grinned. "Wonder where Mamma is?"

The sea elephant in question showed no alarm as the *Geronimo* approached. It was about six or seven feet in length, lumpy and shapeless, and not at all pretty, yet rather appealing in its ugliness.

"No more'n three or four hundred pounds," Boots commented as they began to pass. "There he goes!"

The baby sea elephant, whose sire would likely weigh in excess of five thousand pounds, sank backward into the quiet darkness of the water below. This tail-first sinking is characteristic of the sea elephant and a good means of identification of this animal at sea.

The men aboard the boat saw no sign of either parent, but none had any doubt that the mother, at least, was probably somewhere nearby.

The sea elephant is actually a seal—the largest of the seal family, in fact. It is also by far the clumsiest of that land-clumsy family ashore and without any doubt the ugliest in physical appearance. Though well deserving of the term "elephant" in its name, it is not only for size alone that this name was applied. Mostly it comes from a strange and apparently useless snout appendage which looks something like a modification of the elephant's trunk. This snout is made up of a heavy fatty tissue without much of a muscular structure. As a result, it hangs down eight or nine inches below the animal's mouth.

About the only time this mass of flesh moves of its own accord is when the bull utters his deep, far-carrying roar. The bellow begins far down inside him and seems to erupt from mouth and nose together, causing this flabby trunklike appendage to swell up with air and the tips of it to curl into the animal's mouth. Strangely, this causes the sound to seem as if it is coming from somewhere else, much in the manner in which a ventriloquist throws his voice. Scientists are still not sure exactly how or why this is done.

A large male sea elephant may reach a length of seventeen feet or perhaps even more and his weight may well exceed five thousand pounds. The female, however, rarely gets above ten feet in length.

In water, these animals are curiously graceful despite their bulk and can exhibit a surprising speed and maneuverability. On land, it's an entirely different matter. Few creatures in this world can then vie with it for pure clumsiness and unattractiveness. When it comes ashore, its huge body settles like a plastic bag full of jelly into a more or less formless pile. The coarse and sparsely-haired skin is deeply wrinkled and cracked. When it rolls over onto its side or back, those areas where the front and rear flippers attach to the body seem to be sickly and inflamed, ranging in color from a dingy pinkish-white to a raw-appearing angry red or mottled orange.

For many hours at a time the animal will lie on shore in what seems to be a helpless puddle. Its two prime objectives in life are evidently to sleep and eat. Poking or prodding them while they lie there awake will hardly cause any response. Yet, let someone sharply interrupt its slumber and the strong front flippers are apt to flick rocks and pebbles with slingshot accuracy at the cause of the disturbance. Then it will go back to sleep. The pebble-flicking, however, is more the exception than the rule. Usually the sea elephant will merely lie there without making any effort to move away; in fact, with the creature scarcely indicating an awareness of what is happening.

They can, however, become extremely dangerous to one who becomes too bold. Lazy as they are, they seem incapable of quick action, but let someone get too close with petty annoyances and the massive head may suddenly sweep around in a swift arc which has the punishing power of a battering ram to whatever it strikes. And should the creature take a notion to return to the water, pity the man or beast standing in its way. It will not swerve to avoid such an obstacle, but merely bulldoze itself right over it; and six thousand pounds of blubbery weight can make a permanent impression upon anyone!

The sea elephant appears to delight in lying in the sun and when the time comes for its natural molt, the animal has the appearance of being badly sunburned, even though this is not

the case. Actually, the outermost layer of skin peels off in large blisters with the hair. In these blotched areas of peeling, the new coat is a beautiful silver gray, in marked contrast to the bleached brown and mottled pinkish-orange of its old skin.

Its diet is principally fish. It will descend to quite considerable depths and there, at its leisure, catch and eat a variety of slow-moving creatures—ratfish, squid, dogfish, and a variety of other small sharks. Within its stomach can usually be found a quantity of rocks which it has swallowed and these apparently aid in grinding up the food for digestion, much as pebbles and grit in a bird's crop perform the same function.

As with most of the seal species, the breeding season for sea elephants occurs from around December to March. At this time the males wallow ponderously ashore and are followed a little later by numerous females not much more attractive than they. From among these females the bull selects his harem of cows and for the rest of the breeding season, which lasts for months, there rises an almost constant bedlam of bellowing, bawling, and brawling as they fight among themselves to retain possession of their own cows or lure away someone else's.

For many generations the sea elephant has been slaughtered for its oil-heavy fat—with as much as two hundred gallons of oil being rendered from the fat of a single large bull. As a result, herds that once numbered in the many thousands have today been so decimated in numbers that strict laws regulate their capture even for zoos or scientific study and it is illegal to kill them. Nor is this protection only carried on by the United States. At one time the northern sea elephant on Guadalupe Island off Baja, California, had become so low in numbers that only a drastic move by the Mexican Government saved them from extinction. A company of soldiers was stationed on the island with orders to shoot poachers or anyone else molesting these animals. Still, as with the manatees in Florida, occasionally individuals rising for air are senselessly and needlessly shot by boatmen and it is possible yet that extinction may result if such a practice is not halted.

For Marlin, it had been a distinct pleasure to see the young sea elephant, but now he turned his eyes forward again toward the bulk of Santa Catalina Island which was just becoming visible on the horizon.

There, perhaps, they might find the object of their search—the pilot whale.

Chapter Five

Animals ahead!

The shout came from Boots Calandrino late in the afternoon and the eyes of Marlin Perkins, Frank Brocato, and Benny Falcone followed the outstretched arm of the skipper. Far ahead, well over a mile away, a half dozen or more dark shapes were barely visible as they broke the water surface briefly to breathe.

"Pilots, all right," Brocato grunted. "Thought we'd have to call it quits for the day without seeing any." He turned the wheel slightly and the *Geronimo* nosed directly toward the pod.

For almost six hours they had been following bleak and rather barren coast line of Santa Catalina Island, mostly maintaining a distance of a mile or more from shore. They had seen harbor seals and gulls, cormorants and pelicans, and dozens of cruising blue sharks since first approaching the island. Great patches of floating kelp drifted darkly on the surface and, as they passed them, Marlin had been able to see numerous small squid hanging motionless among the long fronds or darting about among them.

To the side of one such patch of kelp the men saw a huge ocean sunfish, or mola, which would easily have tipped the scales at four hundred pounds. It wasn't by any means so large as the species grew but it was, nevertheless, a large and interesting fish to see. Actually, because of the peculiar shape of its body, it looked less like a whole fish than a fish that had been chopped in half just behind its dorsal fin.

Here and there, too, startled by the approach of the *Geronimo*, flying fishes leaped from the water, spread their wide winglike pectoral fins, and soared neatly over the water. Occasionally their tails would touch the surface in mid-flight and vibrate rapidly to provide them an extra boost along the way. Several of them soared for more than a hundred yards before knifing back under the surface.

It had been interesting seeing these creatures, but until now the water had seemed devoid of any whales. In fact, only a few minutes before the sighting Marlin had said to Boots, "hard to believe that even if we saw whales, they'd allow a boat as large as the *Geronimo* to come up very close to them."

The skipper of the boat had nodded and replied, "I guess it is sort of odd when you come to think of it, especially considering how apparently intelligent an animal they are. Of course they won't ride the bow waves like the dolphins, but often they'll seem to be every bit as curious about us as we are about them. They really have little to fear from, say, a skiff among them, or divers, but they don't seem to like anything coming closer than about fifteen feet away.

"When we're approaching to try to get a noose around them, we try to hold the bowsprit basket about that far in back of them until they go underwater, then gradually pick up speed so that the next time they surface to breathe we'll be at the perfect distance above and behind their heads for tossing the noose-net. Once in a while," he said, with a sudden laugh, "it actually works, too. More often than not, though, they're too cagey to fall for it.

"Now and again," he had continued, "they'll playfully nudge or bump skiffs or other small boats in which someone's trying to get close enough to take pictures. That's rare, though. Usually they'll keep their distance. In most of our encounters, that's one of the big problems. When we come up from behind and try to catch them, they'll lead us on for hours, as if it's a game, staying just a hairsbreadth out of our range. Let's hope those we encounter—if any—won't be in the mood to do that."

Now, as they moved toward the whales, Marlin watched them

through binoculars as the animals continued to rise briefly to breathe and then vanish again beneath the surface. The swiftness with which they could do this was surprising; a quick roll on the surface, which lasted only a second or two would both empty and fill those great lungs. Their ability to remain underwater for long periods was not, however, due entirely to the air in their lungs.

Much of the oxygen inhaled by whales is stored in the hemoglobin of the blood and the myoglobin of the muscle tissues. Land animals, which can breathe as often as they like, have little of this oxygen-holding myoglobin in their muscles and they also ventilate only a fraction of the air in their lungs at one breath. The whale, on the other hand, ventilates almost completely.

When the whale breathes—or "blows," as the process is known —it does not squirt a stream of water from its blow-hole, as so many people believe. There may be some water collected on the top of the closed hole which is blown away when it opens, but this moisture was not inside the whale. The illusion which gave rise to this water-squirting belief comes from whaling operations in cold waters of the North. There, when the whale blows, its breath condenses in the air which is so much colder, much as human breath causes a little cloud of condensation in the wintertime. A spurting stream of fog rises and, from a distance, tends to look like a spray of water from the whale's blow-hole.

There is a distinct popping sound to the blow which sounds something like a sharp sneeze. The single blow-hole of the pilot whale, somewhat crescent-shaped and slightly left of center, opens with that puffing pop and so fast is both exhalation and inhalation that they seem to occur simultaneously. Scientists still have not definitely determined how this is accomplished, but perhaps the research now being carried out at Marineland of the Pacific may one day solve this mystery.

But now, as the *Geronimo* plowed through the swells toward the whales, Boots and Benny became very busy. Their first job was to rig the noose-net lines carefully to the side of the boat in

such a manner that they would be out of the way, yet pull off easily should a whale be lassoed.

This noose-net was an invention of Calandrino and Brocato and it was in large measure responsible for their pronounced success in whale catching. It was as they were on their way out to the island that the two men had rigged it up to be ready, while Benny operated the boat.

It was a deceptively simple affair. A sturdy nylon rope had been formed into a noose having a diameter of about twice the size of the mouth of a bushel basket. To this had been tied a section of sturdy netting to form a belly below the noose about two feet deep. The netting was then tied to the noose at about six-inch intervals with a fairly light cotton line which would break rather easily. Then lead weights of two different sizes were attached to the noose. On the side that would be the bottom, these weights were three-ounce egg-shaped sinkers and those on top were only quarter-ounce.

The long trailing end of the cord which made up the noose had then been securely spliced to three hundred feet of heavy hemp rope coiled in a sizable wooden box on the deck along the starboard rail. This box was near the power winch and a pulley block extending upward from the rail.

And now, with the *Geronimo* nearing the quarry, Boots took the weighted noose-net and moved to the bow of the boat with it, making sure to pass it around the outside of all rigging. Although here the water was choppier and the swells more powerful, nevertheless, he moved out on the narrow bowsprit with agility until he reached the basket, in which he stood up and braced himself. Temporarily anchoring the noose to the basket, he tied the trailing end securely to the cable rigging with line having a breaking test of thirty pounds. In that way the rope was held up out of his way, yet would easily pop free if he was successful in lassoing a whale.

While he did this, Benny was taking care of the rope which led to the box, tying it securely in several places to the starboard rail and rigging. Care had to be taken that this was done in such

manner that when the whale was caught, it would break the line free without that line becoming fouled on any of the rigging, the pulley arm, the rail, or anything else.

By the time they were finished, they had approached to within a hundred yards of the whales. Sure-footedly, Marlin climbed the rigging to the crow's-nest platform and straddled the plank there in order to get a good view of the action taking place below, yet keep himself out of the way.

It was an exciting sight and there seemed to be a tangible sense of tension in the air. Two or three of the whales were poised quietly on the surface, not swimming but just lying there. Not until the *Geronimo* was thirty yards away did they begin to move lazily.

"Sleeping," Brocato called up to Marlin. "They're active both day and night, so they sleep just about anytime, too. Did you notice how that bulging head gives them a sort of controlled buoyancy?"

Marlin nodded and returned his attention to the whales ahead of the boat. It was a small pod with no more than fourteen or fifteen individuals, of which sometimes three or four were surfacing at the same time. They swam not in a cluster but rather in a somewhat ragged straight line, side by side, and perhaps four to eight feet apart. On the mast, Marlin could clearly hear the puffing blast as they breathed and he watched them closely as they performed this function. The shiny black heads would break the surface momentarily and the blow-hole, as it cleared the water during the rolling action, would open only briefly for that explosive gasp.

Now that they were closer Marlin could see that the majority of these whales were much too large. Most were seventeen or eighteen feet in length and one large bull with great bulging head must have been very close to twenty feet long.

Though these pilot whales could have outdistanced the *Geronimo* easily, they did not. The boat's top speed was nine knots but, had it desired to, a pilot whale could have surged away at a speed of twenty to twenty-five knots for a short distance and easily ten knots for a sustained time.

Actually, about the only time the pilot whale swims at its top speed is when it is trying to catch fish, leap (or breach) out of the water, or escape some danger such as the killer whale. A knot of speed is somewhat faster than a mile-per-hour; one knot equalling 6,080 feet-per-hour as opposed to a land mile of 5,280 feet. Therefore, a whale pod cruising at ten knots is actually traveling close to twelve miles-per-hour. There is no such term as "knots-per-hour."

Despite the bursts of speed or sustained travel of ten knots which pilot whales can perform, these animals cause little wake in the water. The bluntly rounded front of the whale's head throws almost no bow wave; their flippers and flukes, along with a highly flexible body and rubbery skin, cause little turbulence. Moreover, the living body of the whale is nearly buoyant and little energy is used to hold the whale's weight up against the pull of gravity.

But even though those whales could have left the *Geronimo* far behind, they preferred to meander along easily now at a speed of three or four knots. Their swimming was efficiently done, powered entirely by the up-and-down motion of the final two-thirds of the body. Every power stroke of the fluke is equally a recovery for the next stroke. They can also swim on rare occasions, especially when injury makes it necessary, with a side-to-side movement of the entire tail stock rather than the normal up-and-down movement of the flukes.

The swimming of the pilot whales, Marlin noted, was more direct and with less twisting and turning than that of the dolphins. Their acceleration was slower than dolphins, but he knew that eventually they can go as fast or perhaps even faster. At Marineland yesterday Marlin had seen one of the whales swim backward by making short, lobsterlike flickings of the tail under the belly. He had also seen them swim on their backs with chin and flipper-tips out of the water. The whales ahead of the boat now, however, did none of those tricks. They merely headed away in that curious straight line.

Out in the bowsprit basket, Boots had been leaning far over the rail with the noose-net in his hands, studying the pod. Now he shook his head, straightened, and began tying the device to the basket again.

"No good, Frank," he called to Brocato. "Too big, every one of 'em. Why can't we come across a pod like this early in the morning?"

Brocato made a face and shook his own head in reply, then looked back and up at Marlin who was still perched on the lookout. "We've considered possibly taking one like this late in the afternoon, trussing him up well to the raft and laying over in the harbor with him overnight before starting back in the morning," he told him, "but we've never gone ahead and done it. Guess we're both afraid it might die before we could get it in and we wouldn't want that to happen. And we sure couldn't start towing one in at this time of day. Too bad, though. There were some beauties in that pod."

Boots was already coming back to the boat from the basket and so Marlin climbed down from the lookout perch and they both joined Brocato at the upper controls. Brocato was spinning the helm to turn the *Geronimo* back to follow in an easterly direction the rugged shore line of the island.

"If we'd gotten a rope around one of those," Boots told Marlin, indicating the rapidly disappearing pod with his thumb, "you'd have seen some unusual behavior from the others. Social organization is very strong among them and when one of the whales is caught, others will do all they can to help him get free. It sounds too humanlike for many people to believe, but it's true.

"A few years ago," he continued, "we caught a nice female about ten feet long and put her in the same tank with Bubbles, Squirt, Bimbo, and some of the others. She was scared to death and swam over to one side of the tank and just lay there for a long while. At first the other whales didn't make any attempt to go near her but then, because they seemed to sense her despair or loneliness or whatever, Bubbles finally swam over and we were amazed to see her come up alongside the new one and touch sides with her. After a few minutes Bubbles made some faint squeaking sounds, put a flipper over the new female's back and swam around the tank with her for three complete turns. You know something, just like that the new one perked up and joined the others and she's been fine ever since."

Brocato nodded, confirming what Boots said and added, "The old-time whalers used to take advantage of this desire they show to help one another. The men found that they could often catch a dozen or more with one lowering of the boats because others came and remained close to the harpooned whale, as if to give aid. Those whalers believed that the blood in the water was the attraction that kept them close, but now we know they were wrong. It was probably sound communication."

This was something Marlin knew about and he agreed. "Apparently they're much like the porpoises and dolphins in being able to communicate. I understand that the scientists at Marineland have catalogued a whole series of vocal sounds made by the pilot whales."

Brocato nodded again. "They've taped a lot of them. Squeals, whistles, buzzing sounds, mewing sounds like a cat, shrill chirps like a bird might make, grating sounds similar to snoring, and even a kind of bellowing roar when the head is out of the water. But here's something you may not know: none of those sounds come from the mouth. The voice box—larynx—probably produces whistling sounds only in the pilot whale but this is by constriction, not by vocal cords. Pilot whales don't have 'em. Neither do any of the other whales or the porpoises and dolphins."

"The sounds come from the blow-hole?" Marlin asked.

"That's right. Air is forced out of the blow-hole by heavy pressure in the lungs or from air vibrated inside the blow-hole passages without escape of the air."

"Don't any sounds at all come from the mouth?"

Boots answered this time. "Yes, but not vocal sounds. The

animal can clap his jaws together with a warning sound that makes a noise like a trunk closing underwater, but it's strictly percussion, not voice box. They can also make a loud kissing sound by smacking the lips of the blow-hole and another sort of muffled explosion sound by striking the water surface with the flukes."

They continued to discuss at length the communicating sounds made by whales and Marlin was amazed at the amount of information gained at Marineland from the captive whales. Communication is very important between them because they are a highly social creature, but such communication is not strictly limited to voice. They also communicate by signals or signs which mean as much among them as a frown or shrug of the shoulders or motion of the hand means among human beings.

Even such actions as rolling over, spinning in the water, tumbling and at the same time flashing the light spot on the chest, are all signals which may have definite meanings among the whales. So may certain movements of the mouth, flippers, and flukes.

A sign or sound of communicative nature must, of course, always have the same meaning in order to be understood by another individual and gain desired results from him. The pilot whales, insofar as can be determined to date, have no abstract spoken words. Every sound made has a very simple meaning on the emotional level. While these whales seem to be able to remember things for a long time and respond to new things in a new manner and with new sounds, there is no indication that they discuss such things among themselves later. Only when the physical stimulus for such a movement or sound comes again do they react in the same way, seemingly more through instinct than through any highly advanced degree of intellectual deduction or reasoning.

The pilot whales—and all other whales, too—communicate more by voice than by visible sign. The reason for this is simply that eyesight, even that of a whale, is limited underwater to only about one hundred fifty feet, even under the most ideally clear water conditions. In murky, disturbed water, of course, it is much less. Visibility also decreases rapidly with depth. But sound underwater travels very rapidly and over great distances, and much faster than it does in air. By the time an air-borne sound at sea level has traveled just a shade over a thousand feet, a water-borne sound made at the same time has traveled close to a mile!

So far as researchers have been able to understand them, the whale sounds seem to fit these categories: the chirp, whistle, and piping sounds are used in warning others or calling for help; the whine or mewing cry is associated with sexual activity, and the smacking of the nostril (or blow-hole) signifies contentment. The grating sound, similar to a rusty hinge or sharp snoring is used for echo-ranging and location, much as the dolphins do. There is no escape of air during this sound. It comes from the sealed nasal chambers and is produced by high-frequency vibrations. When tape recorded and played back at slower speed, it sounds like a series of rapid clicks.

The roaring these whales can make with their heads out of water is apparently not a natural sound but rather one they have learned to make at Marineland. At such a time the mouth is open and the entire head is out of water when the sound is made, but though it seems to issue from the mouth, it does not; as with the others, it comes from the blow-hole.

All of these sounds, scientists have found, can be reduced to three basic types: barks, whistles, and clicks, but with a wide degree of variations and combinations.

The fact that they had not been able to take any of the whales from this pod of such large creatures was, of course, a big disappointment to Marlin and the crew, but there was no help for it. Now, as they fell silent, Marlin turned his attention to a closer inspection of Santa Catalina Island.

This island is roughly hour-glass shaped, running from east to west. It is about twenty-two miles long and perhaps eight miles wide at the widest portion. In the center where it pinches together—an area called the Isthmus—it is only a half mile wide and quite low. It is, in fact, the only low ground on the entire island. At this place a natural harbor forms on either side of the

Isthmus and the harbor on the south side, called Catalina Harbor, was where the *Geronimo* was now headed to anchor for the night.

There are not many places along the entire shore line of the island for safe overnight anchorage. Two such places are the harbors on either side of the Isthmus, and another is the harbor at the town of Avalon. That town is the only well-populated community on the whole island and it is located at the southeastern end. There are, however, a handful of homes at the Isthmus.

Santa Catalina Island, Marlin decided, could not accurately be termed a paradise. It is very mountainous, has virtually no trees and is mostly a highly arid terrain. Great quantities of the succulent prickly-pear cactus grow all over its surface, along with a coarse buffalo grass. With few exceptions, the shore line is sheer cliff which plunges into water of great depth with no beaches and rarely even a rocky or stony shore line that is level. Within mere yards of many shore areas the water is twelve hundred feet in depth. The only places where even semblances of

level though rocky shore lines exist are areas where steep arroyos meet the ocean. On these areas the seals tend to congregate in large numbers.

The very depth of the water along this rugged shore line attracts a wide variety of marine creatures. Fish of many species are here in abundance and there is an amazing quantity of squid in these waters. Since squid are the principal food of the pilot whales, it follows that the whales frequent this area as well. As a result, more pilot whales have been taken alive off the shore line of Catalina Island than any other place.

"Hearing," said Frank Brocato suddenly, breaking the spell of island-staring Marlin was engaged in, "is the whale's most important and relied-upon sense. But vision is very important, too, especially when it comes to catching food. Actually it plays a greater role at such a time than hearing does, or at least so we believe. After catching some of these whales and studying them closely, we learned some pretty interesting things about their power of sight.

"As closely as we can determine, the hunting they do for squid or fish is done almost entirely by eyesight, although the co-ordination of the pod's movement is probably sound controlled. We've found out that they can see very well through water alone and almost as well through air alone, but it's a bit more difficult for them to see through both water and air at the same time, as when they are trained to jump for food held out over the water.

"Their vision through the water and out into the air can be done fairly well when the eyes are just under the surface and there aren't any ripples or waves. You've probably experienced that yourself in your scuba or skin diving."

Marlin nodded and Brocato went on without pause: "But when the water's rough or you're off to one side, double vision like that is extremely difficult or, in many cases, impossible. It takes a lot of practice to train one of our whales to jump accurately and grab a fish held high up in the air. Part of the reason is that the whale's eyes are slightly below the widest part of the head. That makes it easier for him to see what is below than to see what is above him. And as far as being able to see what is immediately in front of his head or directly over his back is concerned, he's blind to those areas. That's another reason we're able to get the bowsprit basket right over them. They can judge by sound exactly how far the prow of the boat is behind them, but they don't realize that twenty-six feet in front of that, the bowsprit basket is hanging right over them."

"Their eyes, incidentally," Boots interjected, "can move and see independently of one another. They have thick, rubbery eyelids, but no eyelashes at all. In the cornea of the eye there is a dark sort of flap or shield in the cornea over the pupil. This is part of the iris and as nearly as we can determine, this shades the pupil and protects the retina from the glare when the whale is close to the surface. That pupil expands and contracts much as a human being's does, but it can also narrow down to a horizontal slit and we're still not completely sure why. When they're mad or scared, I've seen them roll their eyes just as a horse or dog will do when frightened or angry. Better watch out when that happens, too!"

Again the conversation tapered off as they neared the harbor at the Isthmus. When they pulled in and anchored there, Captain Brocato surprised Marlin with another talent. He became the cook and did an admirable job. From the store of fresh supplies he made delicious salads and Italian main dishes as good as or even better than might have been obtained in the finest Italian restaurant. Cooking was done on a little charcoal grill set up on the deck and the food, after a full day afloat on the sea, was some of the best Marlin could ever remember eating.

After dinner, Boots, Benny, and Marlin went ashore in the skiff and ambled about in the little Isthmus settlement, which is dominated by a cluster of neat and unusually well-preserved military barracks built by the United States Government during the Civil War.

Despite its arid nature, there is a surprising variety of wildlife on the island, of which Marlin was able to see wild goat herds, a species of large gray ground squirrel, quail, doves, and a few of the transplanted herds of American bison; all of which apparently do quite well here. There were also, Benny said, quite a few wild pigs throughout the island.

Near the scattered swellings on the Isthmus grew a number of towering and graceful eucalyptus trees planted there by the inhabitants. Although some hunting is done on the island, it is largely a sanctuary. Actually a part of Los Angeles County, Santa Catalina Island is privately owned by a single person—P. K. Wrigley, the chewing gum tycoon.

At dusk, Marlin, Boots, and Benny returned to the *Geronimo*. He didn't know how they felt, but Marlin thought it heavenly to stretch out in the bunk below deck in the prow and relax. It had been a long and very tiring day.

Tomorrow the search for a whale would resume.

Chapter Six

The following day, with their search for a whale begun at dawn, was a disappointing one, as were the two days after that. Neither individual whale nor pod was sighted during these three days. On two occasions, however, there were intervals of excitement and amusement when bottlenose dolphins flanked the *Geronimo*, paced the boat, and clowned about in the water with incredible speed and agility. Although the craft was traveling at near top speed, the dolphins had no difficulty keeping pace while at the same time performing such feats as turning in circles, going back and forth under the boat, and taking breath-taking leaps out of the water at the bow. On at least a half dozen occasions the men aboard the *Geronimo* watched as one or more of the animals actually swam on his side or back and appeared intent upon trying to see who—or what—was standing on deck.

At one point Boots claimed with a straight face that he saw one of the dolphins wink at him, which set Brocato and Marlin into gales of laughter. Beyond any doubt, the mammals were interesting to see and for some time during the afternoon of the second day all three men discussed at length the intelligent creatures and the penetrating research scientists were presently conducting to learn more about their habits, abilities, and intelligence.

"Their echo-ranging ability is incredible," Brocato said, "and so far man's only scratched the surface in trying to duplicate it."

"No doubt about it," Boots added, "we can learn a lot from them and there's extensive dolphin research going on right now all over the world. It's altogether possible that in studying them—as we've been doing in such places as China Lake, California, and Woods Hole, Massachusetts, to say nothing of our own Marineland—we may be able to find the key to help us unlock a great many secrets of the sea."

On both occasions that the dolphins paced the *Geronimo*, they stayed only a quarter-hour or so and then left, apparently tiring of sporting with the steadily moving boat. Marlin was sorry they had left so soon, but there were other things to see.

Sharks, for example, were abundant in these waters—particularly the blue sharks, which often cruised about on the surface with dorsal fin and tail sticking out of the water. They were an ominous and yet intriguing sight and Marlin, for one, never tired of watching them. Nevertheless, the keen enthusiasm that had filled all four men the first couple of days was now becoming a little dulled. The day can be long and tiring when hour after hour the eye scans the water surface in all directions for whales and spots nothing but an occasional dolphin or the seemingly ever-present blue sharks.

But then, later on their fourth day out, they were rewarded by a relatively close sighting of a huge thresher shark, which came casually to the surface and momentarily allowed the top seven feet of its amazingly long tail to project out of the water.

Undoubtedly one of the most peculiar tails in nature is that of the thresher shark. The upper lobe of the tail is longer than the rest of the shark's body and it serves a useful function in the capturing of prey.

The shark more or less "rides herd" on a school of fish which he intends to attack, circling round and round them until he has forced them to cluster together in a dense mass. Then he goes in for the kill. Darting suddenly into the midst of the fish, the thresher slashes his tail furiously back and forth, killing or severely injuring any fish struck. Then, as the rest of the panic-stricken school flees, he turns to feed upon the dead and injured that have been left behind.

Occasionally such sharks will even use this deadly tail weapon to strike sea birds and larger fish. There is no basis for the belief, however, that threshers will team up with swordfish to attack whales or men in small boats.

"They're not particularly dangerous to man, even when he's in the water," Boots Calandrino said. "At least not like some of the other shark species, such as the white shark, for example. But they're another sea animal that the commercial fishermen don't like at all because they so often tear up the nets. Glad you got a chance to see this one, though, Marlin."

"Interesting to see," Marlin Perkins responded, "but right about now I'd have gladly passed it up for a chance at some whales."

That chance didn't come right away, however, and when the fourth day showed every indication of the sea's being just as devoid of whales as the previous three, Marlin suggested they take a break in their searching and liven things up with some shark activity. Brocato, Boots, and Benny were quick to agree. Sharks were in abundance everywhere, the majority of them being blue sharks ranging from four to six feet in length, but with some individuals as large as eight or ten feet. All of them were nasty customers.

"We get some hammerhead and soup-fin sharks in these waters and, of course, some threshers like the one we saw yesterday. Occasionally some big whites, too," Brocato grimaced as he mentioned the name of the big man-eater, "but the blue is by far the most common around here."

Those blue sharks were easy to spot on the surface. They would

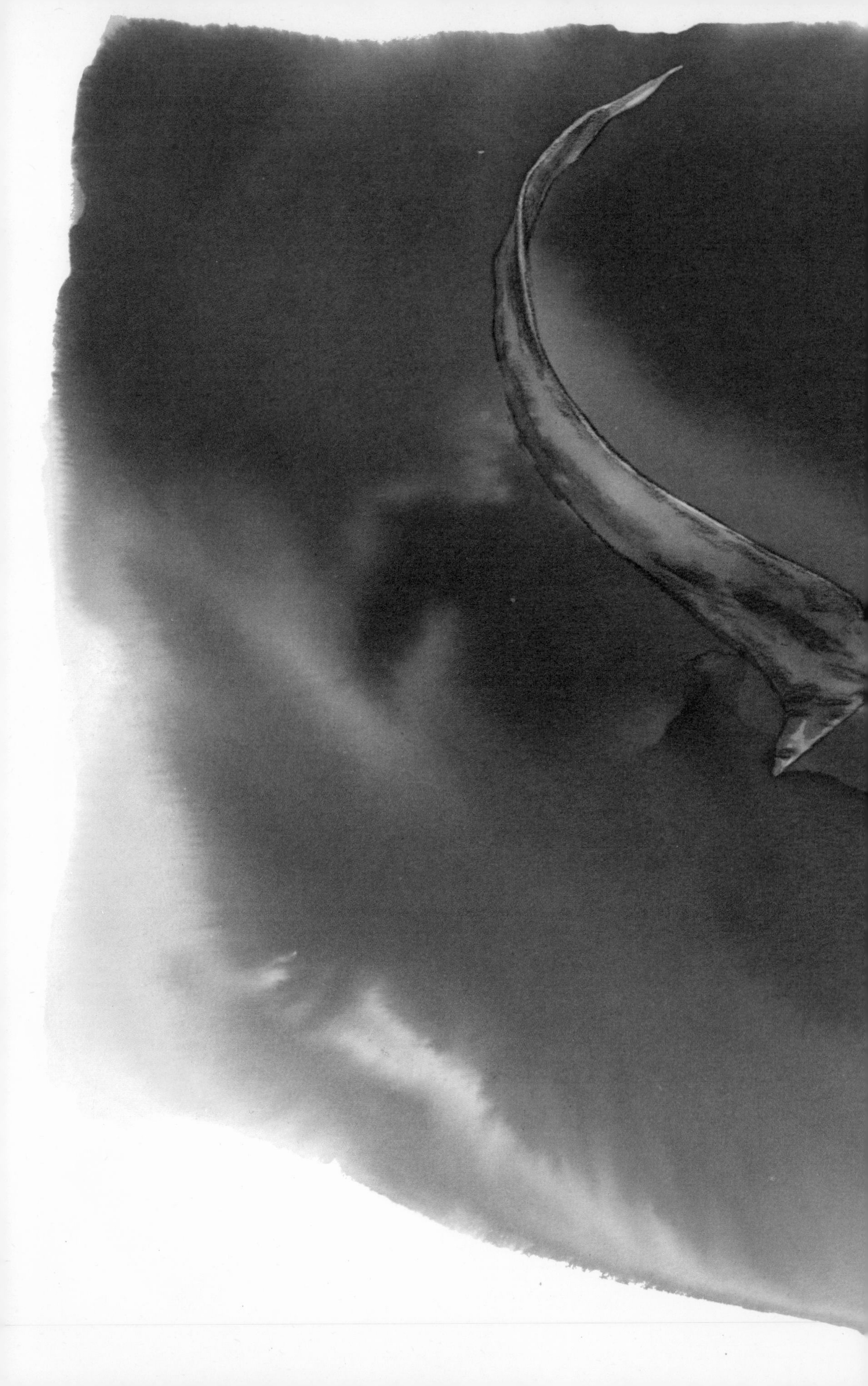

cruise about with just their dorsal fin and the top of the tail showing above the water. Whenever the *Geronimo* came within ten or fifteen yards of them, however, they would become frightened and flash away.

"They're about the most cowardly fish in these waters," Brocato continued, indicating a four-foot blue with a dip of his head. "They're scared of their own shadows. But," and now his voice hardened in dislike, "let 'em smell blood in the water and they go crazy. Then they attack anything and you can't even beat 'em off. Seems as if they go mad whenever there's fresh blood around. You'll see."

Boots tossed out a strong hand line ending in a hook baited with anchovy. The heavy sinker quickly pulled it down and within minutes something solid struck the bait. Expertly he fought it and drew it flopping onto the deck of the *Geronimo*. It was a nice bonito of seven or eight pounds. Brocato turned off the motor

and the *Geronimo* drifted lazily on the swells. Hardly a ripple was stirring the surface now.

Quickly Boots rigged up a noose on a long aluminum pole which he handed to Marlin. He cut off the tail third of the bonito then and tied it to a cord on the end of another aluminum pole, and then tossed the bait into the water and began dragging it on the surface just in front of Marlin's loop. Benny held the remainder of the fish's carcass over the side so that the large quantity of blood would drain into the water.

As soon as the fish was drained of blood, Benny cut some small chunks from it and at intervals tossed them into the water. It didn't take long to get a reaction. First there was a momentary flash from far below as a large creature turned on its side and snatched a chunk of the freely sinking meat. In a moment it was joined by another shape and then a third. Within fifteen minutes the water around the boat was alive with the sinister sharp-nosed and streamlined shapes of the blue sharks.

Oblivious of the loop Marlin held in the water, they darted swiftly at the bait Boots was dragging and began tearing it apart, striking savagely at it with gaping jaws and trying to rip it away. Boots was hard put to keep them from yanking the pole out of his hands. He moved the bait closer to the noose and then, very neatly, a six-foot blue shark thrust the front third of his body through Marlin's noose to get at the bait.

With a hard jerk, Marlin snapped the loop tightly around him and the fight was on. The shark churned the water to a white froth in its struggles to get away, but Marlin hung on grimly and gradually maneuvered the big fish to the side of the boat. With Benny helping him, he raised the fish enough so that Boots could grab the tail. Brocato went to Boots's side to help him and with much grunting and tugging, the four men managed to bring the fish flopping to the deck of the *Geronimo*.

At once Benny Falcone opened the hatch which led to the huge live well in the belly of the boat. A seven-foot cubicle, the live well held seven and a half tons of water which constantly changed itself with water from the sea around them. Many thousands of fine living specimens of marine life had been returned to Marineland of the Pacific within this compartment, ranging from sharks and rays to fish of all kinds and even large octopi.

With some difficulty the noose was loosened from the shark and Boots, still holding the tail, maneuvered the savage animal headfirst into the live well and let go.

"Shark that size could take a healthy chunk out of a man," he said, closing the hatch and then straightening. "You still want to go down for some pictures, Marlin?"

Marlin nodded, handed Benny his pole, and entered the cabin at once to don his rubber scuba-diving suit. The water of the sea here was not especially cold, but Marlin's suit would help ward off the penetrating chill which almost necessarily accompanies immersion for any length of time.

While Marlin changed, Boots and Benny attached the heavy shark cage to the winch, pausing every now and then to toss another chunk of the bonito to the sharks in order to keep them milling around. There were now easily two or three dozen sharks of all sizes around the boat and beneath it.

In a few minutes Marlin emerged from the cabin, strapping his scuba tanks to himself. He ducked his head and stepped into the steel cage, which looked rather like an elongated bird cage, and then stood erect. Benny handed him his waterproof camera and then, together, Boots and Benny put the steel-mesh door in place and firmly anchored it. Finally, they attached a safety line of heavy nylon rope to the cage in the event that somehow the winch boom should break or the cable snap.

There was not a great deal of room in the cage for Marlin. It was not much more than three feet in diameter, permitting him to stand but not bend over or do much turning around. He checked his camera carefully and, satisfied, adjusted his face mask and clenched his teeth on the scuba mouthpiece and began breathing through it. Everything checked out well and he nodded.

Boots handed him a chunk of the bonito to draw the sharks toward him and then the cage was carefully raised. Boots and Benny swung it so the boom pivoted and the cage was hanging over the water. Then the winch was reversed and the cage lowered.

Marlin had anticipated that going down in the shark cage would be an exciting experience, but it was almost too exciting. The sharks were everywhere and in a virtual frenzy to get the chunk of bonito Marlin held. He thrust it out through the bars and there was a frantic rush by at least half a dozen of the sharks to get the morsel.

Tails and bodies slammed against the cage with jarring impact and one after another Marlin snapped pictures. The water was a clear bright blue and he could see for a considerable distance. Everywhere he looked there were sharks and others still coming. And now, with the fish chunks gone, the sharks turned their undivided attention upon Marlin.

With dogged persistence and considerable strength, they butted his cage. They thrust their sharp snouts through the bars in an

effort to get at him, jerking their heads back and forth viciously and then more and more determinedly slamming themselves against the cage.

And suddenly it was no longer a pleasantly exciting experience. The cage was being bounced about so badly that Marlin was slammed from side to side by the blows. Snouts thrust toward him, which were fortunately stopped by the bars that had a span of four or five inches between them, nevertheless still managed occasionally to strike him with hammerlike blows on his arms, legs, and back.

Marlin heard a faint metallic clink and then saw to his dismay that with the impact of an especially hard blow by one of the larger blue sharks, an upright bar of his cage had snapped at the point where it had been welded to the circumference frame. Another blow at the same spot might dislodge it completely or even break loose another bar. If that happened, the resultant opening would be large enough for one of the small or medium-sized sharks to thrust its head in and grab Marlin himself.

It was an unnerving situation. When there came a brief pause in their buffeting attacks, Marlin quickly reached out and gripped the nylon safety line attached to the barring above him. He jerked the line hard—once, twice, three times. Nothing happened. He jerked again and still nothing happened. The nylon line had merely absorbed the tugs at the rail of the *Geronimo* and no one aboard detected the signals. From on deck they could see the cage clearly and all looked well. It was not possible for them to detect the break in the one bar.

Meanwhile, Marlin's predicament had abruptly worsened. From out of the dim distance cruised another shark—a very large one. It was not another blue shark this time, but rather the dreaded white shark, the most notorious man-eater of the shark world. Fully twenty feet in length, it drifted smoothly toward the cage and the tiny, low-slung eyes regarded the occupant coldly. The other sharks pulled away a little to continue their circling at a more respectful distance.

It almost seemed, as the great deadly fish poised there contemplating the cage and Marlin within, that it was trying to decide how best to attack. It eased itself closer to the cage, though still mostly hidden from those above by the bulk of the boat. There, with its snout no more than two feet from the cage, it stopped at eye level to Marlin. The great gill slits were pulsing rhythmically and the tremendous multitoothed mouth opened about a foot and then closed again.

Marlin had undergone many exciting and sometimes frightening experiences with large animals in the wilds before, but never one quite so frightening as staring eye-to-eye at so close a distance with a creature so powerful that it could easily smash this cage and one bite of those fantastic jaws could chop him in half.

As if sensing what it had to do, the white shark began moving slowly away. At perhaps a dozen feet it turned and again regarded its caged quarry. It seemed that the muscles of the fish were bunching for a powerful drive which would slam it with pile-driver force into the cage.

And then the cage lifted!

With what seemed excruciating slowness, the winch brought up the cage. The white shark still had plenty of time to attack, but now it seemed suspicious of the movement and remained where it was, watching.

The cage broke the surface and then, a moment later, it was entirely out of the water and being swung aboard. The nimble fingers of Boots and Benny released the gate catches and opened the door screening. Marlin removed his mouthpiece, pushed his face mask high up on his head and handed his camera to Benny.

"Get your pictures all right?" Boots asked, grinning.

Marlin smiled in return and blew out a deep breath of air. He nodded and then tapped the broken bar of the shark cage with a finger. "Next time, though," he said, "I think I'll let someone else have the honors."

Chapter Seven

Three more days passed, and though occasional pods of whales were seen and pursued, bad luck seemed to plague Marlin and the crew of the *Geronimo*.

On two of these days the whales were skittish and just would not allow the boat to get near them—at least not near enough to attempt a capture. As soon as the boat got within twenty or thirty yards of them, the whales would sound. Mainly this skittishness was due to the weather. A heavy overcast had formed and hung low over the slightly choppy surface, causing the normally deep blue water to look dark and gray.

Boots shook his head in exasperation. "Unless this choppiness settles and these clouds lift a little or break up," he told Marlin, "we're not even going to be able to get close to them. When it's bright and calm and they can see the boat, they're not so much afraid and we can get right next to them. It's when the sky is dark and the surface kicks up that visibility gets bad for them. They can hear the sound of the motor approaching, but they can't see the boat well and so they get frightened. Just as they are now."

Marlin could see Boots was right. It was obvious the whales had no intention of letting the boat get too near to them. While in clearer weather they had been able to approach so closely that the bowsprit basket had been right over them, now they were sounding when the basket was still many yards away. Then, far below the surface they would change direction and not surface again for three or four minutes. When they did, they would be a half mile or more distant and moving away at a rapid rate.

Although the pilot whale spends the majority of his life beneath the surface of the sea, it is an air breather and must, of course, come to the surface regularly to breathe. During normal activities it will surface for air from about every thirty seconds to two minutes.

"They can stay down a good bit longer than that," said Boots. "A few years ago we got our rope on one whale which went almost straight down until he had taken twelve hundred feet of line. He stayed down for four minutes and fifty seconds, which is the longest submersion we've ever timed at sea.

"We thought that was a record, but one day at Marineland Bimbo proved us wrong. He went down to the bottom of his tank and stayed there for ten minutes. So as far as we know, that must be just about the maximum time limit under water."

This exasperating condition of the whales taking fright and sounding at the approach of the boat lasted until just after noon on their seventh day out. Then, while the clouds did not break, they lifted and became considerably thinner, so that once more the water became a deep blue in color. The *Geronimo* was, at this time, near the farthermost point of the island, which is called the West End. Here there were sheer jagged cliffs, such as Ribbon Rock, which plunged a thousand feet or more straight into water as deep as these walls were high.

In front of Ribbon Rock—so named because the strata of alternating light and dark material show so clearly—they found a pod of perhaps thirty pilot whales no more than three hundred

yards distant from the cliffs. Even from where they were, the men aboard the boat could hear the deep booming thunder as powerful swells smashed against the walls and burst into great blossoms of white spray that often shot forty or fifty feet into the air.

The entire bluff area at this point was known as Bull Head and it was an area in which the squid were abundant; therefore, an area often visited by hungry pilot whales. As if delighting in the change in both the sky and calming of the sea, they moved about in all directions, showing themselves at intervals of only a minute or so as they broke the surface for air before continuing their feeding. And this time they seemed not at all perturbed at the approach of the *Geronimo*.

It was again much too late in the day to attempt taking a large adult, but in this pod there were eight or nine big females with calves swimming beside them. Once again Boots and Benny rigged the noose-net in a hurry and Boots clambered out onto the bowsprit and took his position in the basket at the end. The swells were a little heavier today than usual and they had not diminished much even with the relative calming of the water. The boat rose and dipped and the basket in which Boots rode was sometimes as much as fifteen or eighteen feet over the water and at other times plunged downward so steeply that the bottom of the basket smacked into the water and the sea swirled about his booted feet.

Frank Brocato, at the controls, guided the boat with incredible skill, following and anticipating the movements of a particular whale and making every effort to have the basket containing Boots directly over the spot where the whale would next rise to breathe.

The cast Boots was preparing to make would have to be a good one. If the noose-net touched the whale without looping around it, an immediate alarm would shrill out from the one touched and in bare instants the pod would take alarm and flee.

Nor was it simply a matter of getting the boat into position over the whale. Everything had to be timed to perfection. It would be of no benefit to get right over the whale if, at the moment it rose to breathe, a swell raised the bowsprit basket nearly twenty feet off the water. To try to cast the net accurately then was hopeless. By the same token, should the bowsprit dip in the lee of a swell at just the moment the whale was rising, the distance between Boots and the animal would be so slight that the whale would take alarm and sound. The approach had to be timed so that just as the bowsprit basket got over the whale, it was holding steady at about six feet off the water, with the front of the basket just a foot or two behind the rising whale's head.

The complexity of the maneuver was amazing, and Marlin shook his head as he clung to his crow's-nest perch. Little wonder, he thought, that so few pilot whales had ever been caught alive. It was, in fact, just short of incredible that any had been taken at all. Now, from his high perch, he could clearly see the shadowy forms of a half dozen or more whales ten feet or so under the surface just ahead of the bowsprit.

Gently Brocato throttled down to match exactly the boat's speed with that of the whale upon which Boots was now concentrating. The older man's strong hands spun the helm wheel back and forth with great energy, matching each maneuver of the whale, and a high pitch of excitement began to grip everyone aboard. It looked as if this time the fates might be with them.

The whale they were following was a fine young animal, probably not more than a few inches longer than nine feet. At such size it would have been weaned by now and, though obviously it was the offspring of the large female only four feet away to one side, able now to take solid food on its own. Such a youngster would probably adapt excellently to life in the giant tanks at Marineland.

A dozen of the whales, including this mother and youngster, had broken the surface to breathe just as the basket carrying Boots was no more than ten feet behind them. It was a crucial time. If any one of the whales became frightened at a glimpse of the basket hanging above and behind, it would give the alarm squeal and the whole pod would dive.

They didn't! With great puffing gasps they replenished their air supply and slid gracefully beneath the surface to a depth of seven or eight feet and continued their same forward speed. Now, if some vagrant swell did not trick him, Boots had a good chance of connecting.

And so he did.

The whales angled toward the surface to breathe and Boots leaned far out over the rail of the basket, poised with the noose-net held at precisely the right position. Simultaneously seven of the whales surfaced, thrusting three-fourths of their heads out of the water. In that fractional instant Boots acted.

The noose-net shot from his hands as if leaping away with a

life of its own, just as the young whale began breaking surface. While the animal was still in its upward movement, the noose-net dropped over its head. Now the importance of the difference in size of the weights on the noose-net rim became obvious. The small weights on top struck the whale's head about midway between the end of the snout and the blow-hole. The larger weights dropped a foot or so ahead of the animal.

The whale was a powerful young male, and the instant he felt the small weights and netting touch his head he spurted forward. But in that bare instant of time, the heavier weights had carried the forward part of the noose-net down below the whale's head. Thrusting himself forward as he did, the little whale had only plunged his head more deeply into the netting and enabled the noose proper to encircle the animal almost as far back as the dorsal fin.

Boots's timing was flawless. He yanked hard on the rope, and the noose tightened securely around the whale. Instantly the animal gave vent to a sharp whistling squeal and drove for the bottom with a still greater burst of power. So swiftly that the action couldn't be followed, the lengths of thirty-pound-test line holding the nylon rope to the rail of the boat popped as if they were cotton thread and the strong rope disappeared rapidly into the water.

Within just a second or two the hundred feet of nylon lead rope was gone from sight and now the heavier hemp rope was buzzing out of the box in which it was coiled and hissing over the rail. Fifty, a hundred, a hundred fifty feet of the hemp rope were gone and still the line slid away. At two hundred feet the speed at which it was stripping away decreased sharply and at two hundred fifty feet it stopped entirely and the line, instead of going straight down, began angling away from the *Geronimo*.

It was a crucial moment, and now it was Benny's turn for action. While this brief moment of slackness lasted he scooped up the hemp rope and thrust it through the pulley of the stubby block-pulley arm projecting from the rail. In almost the same movement he flipped a coil around the slowly revolving winch drum and snubbed it tight.

By that time Boots had left the bowsprit and was back to him, helping him. Now the heavy hemp rope had become taut again and the *Geronimo* lurched slightly with the pressure put on by the young whale. Brocato, still at the controls, maneuvered to keep the rope from being drawn under the boat and fouling around the prop. More and more of the rope in the water was becoming visible now as the whale continued coming toward the surface.

And then, some three hundred feet off the starboard bow, there he was!

He broke from the water, nearly clearing the surface and causing a tremendous splash. Unable to shake the noose off, he struggled on the surface against the heavy drag it was exerting against him. The rope formed a great arc on the surface from whale to boat, and white foam formed where it entered the water and was being pulled along so sharply through the surface.

The other whales had surfaced now too, several hundred feet away, and were milling about in a frightened manner. Their breathing, as they broke into the air, was accompanied by a series of wheezing, whistlelike sounds, and they were obviously greatly concerned. But one of them—apparently the young whale's mother—took the initiative. She charged through the water in greyhound plunges, sometimes nearly leaving the water.

In a moment she was between the boat and her offspring and had turned to come up alongside the young one. She butted the rope harshly time and again, attempting to knock the tight loop off her baby, but in this she was unsuccessful. And now, having used so much of his energy in those frantic first minutes, the little whale was tiring and could no longer very well resist the inexorable pull of the winch.

Gradually the young male was brought closer to the boat, but the mother whale neither left his side nor stopped her efforts at trying to knock the rope free. A desperate crying sound came from them both that was heart-rending to hear.

At about fifty yards the baby whale seemed to get his second wind and he began struggling sharply again, thrusting himself up in frantic jumps and churning the surface to a froth. The activity did not last long, however, and within another fifteen minutes he

had been brought up beside the boat. Still the mother circled about wildly only a few yards away.

Now Frank Brocato left the controls and joined Boots and Benny on the deck. As that pair held the whale close alongside,

Brocato swiftly dropped another hemp rope noose over the side and, after two tries, managed to get it over the animal's tail and snub it up tightly. Boots, in turn, dropped another rope loop over the young animal's head and then they had him snugly anchored. As if realizing his hopeless position, the little whale abruptly stopped struggling and lay quietly.

The mother continued to move back and forth all around and

under the boat, sometimes even brushing the hull with her seventeen-foot bulk. All the while between her and the young one there was an interchange of sounds: clicking sounds and squalls, sharp explosive cries, and odd whistling sounds.

While Brocato tended the ropes, Boots and Benny quickly activated the boom and swung the large pipe-edged canvas stretcher over the side. Gently, yet with speed and expertness,

they maneuvered it until the bed of the stretcher was under the whale. Then, utilizing the winch again, they raised stretcher and whale and swung the whole thing aboard.

In another moment they had lowered the stretcher onto the mattress Benny spread out on the deck along the rail. A faint trace of blood stained the rope snubbed around the tail, but it came from just a little rope burn that was not serious. Otherwise the animal seemed to be in good shape.

They had their whale!

Chapter Eight

The whale was aboard, all right, and Marlin hustled down from his lookout perch to get a close-up view of it. In just the brief moments that it took him to get down to the deck, however, triumph had abruptly become disaster.

The blow-hole of the little whale remained tightly closed. Two, three, then five minutes passed and the whale did not breathe.

"Shock," Boots said grimly, and he and Marlin slapped the whale's head vigorously in an effort to snap the whale out of the spell in which it lay. There was no response. For another ten minutes they worked over it frantically, but to no avail.

The little whale was dead.

A deep, numbing depression and sorrow filled all four of the men, and they stared soberly at one another and then at the little whale. None of them would have had this happen for anything in the world. Benny and Boots shook their heads and Frank Brocato spoke softly, directing his words to Marlin but talking to all of them.

"They're strange creatures," he said. "In many respects so much like human beings. They seem to have emotions much like ours and are just as susceptible to shock. Ninety-nine times out of a hundred, a young whale like this wouldn't have been bothered too much by all that happened. Oh, he might've been frightened and exhausted from the struggle, but that's all. As soon as he saw he was caught, he would've stopped struggling and then allowed himself to be lifted aboard and taken it without any problem whatever. Strange that this little fellow should have died."

He squatted beside the young whale and patted the rubbery skin of the great rounded head. "Poor little pilot," he said. "It's too bad we—" He broke off sharply with a little exclamation. "Huh! Look here. Maybe we weren't so much to blame after all!"

He pointed at a round pinkish-white break in the skin of the whale's head, between blow-hole and snout. A faint trace of blood showed there and the dense blubber beneath was visible. It was definitely a hole. Boots and Benny nodded knowingly, but Marlin's brow furrowed in puzzlement.

"Been shot," Brocato explained. "That's a bullet hole. It happens a lot, but that's the first one we've caught like that. Easier to understand now why it went into shock and died."

"But who would shoot a whale like that?" protested Marlin. "What possible reason could anyone have for shooting a whale?"

Brocato indicated Boots with a thumb and Boots nodded and began to explain to Marlin while Brocato climbed back to his seat on the upper deck, moved the throttle to full, and headed them directly out to sea.

"Unfortunately," Boots told Marlin, as the pair and Benny gripped the rigging to balance themselves against the sudden increased pitching of the *Geronimo* against the swells, "there are a lot of people who will. Maybe we wouldn't agree with them, but they feel justified in doing it."

"Who?" Marlin persisted, almost angrily.

"Well," Boots said, "you see, this is a squidding area. Catalina

Island waters are a great spawning area for these marine animals. Squid fishermen from hundreds of miles around come here to spread their nets for squid. Mostly the fishing boats are anchored up during the day and we don't see 'em much, but they're around. At night six or seven squid boats drop their nets and then hang big powerful arc lights over the sides of the boats.

"The squid are the *Loligo opalescens* variety, opalescent squid, which are attracted in enormous numbers to the lights, just like moths. Ten of thousands of them come in, and it's not unusual for these commercial boats to get two or three tons of squid in a single night."

They had climbed up to join Brocato as Boots was talking and

now Brocato confirmed what the younger man was saying. "You see, the squid are very important to the fishermen, but they're the prime food of the pilot whales, too. These whales can apparently detect the presence of squid from quite a considerable distance—maybe even through miles of water. They don't do it by sight, obviously, but they don't do it by smell, either, which is what most of these commercial fishermen believe. The pilot whale does not have a sense of smell. It has no olfactory lobes in the brain, so no matter how pungent a smell might be in the air, it can't detect it by breathing. But evidently they have a tremendous sense of taste. When the squid congregate in large numbers, tiny particles of themselves fill the water and drift down-

current. These chemical particles are what the tongue of the pilot whale detects, and thus the pods can follow the taste to its source."

He shook his head sadly. "They find the squid congregating under the lights on the boats and the entire pod rushes in to feed on them. Not only do they disperse the squid, but they tear the nets of the squidders to pieces. And don't think a big pod of whales can't put a dent in the squid population, either. Take Bimbo, back at Marineland, for example. We feed him upward of two hundred pounds of squid a day, and he'd eat more if he could get it!

"Naturally," he added, "the squid fishermen around these waters here get pretty mad about the damage the whales do to the nets and the squid schools. Doesn't do much good to talk conservation to them. It's a matter of economics. This is how they make their living and the whales interfere and cause them to lose money. So most of the squidders have guns handy and when the whales start surfacing nearby for air, they shoot at 'em. Guess I'd find myself doing the same if I were in their place.

"Usually," he added hastily, "they only use .22-caliber rifles or handguns. These'll sting the whales pretty good but they won't normally do any permanent damage. A .22 slug won't go much farther than through the blubber. Now and then, though, some of the squidders get so mad they start using heavier stuff—deer rifles or big revolvers. This is an example of what happens then." He touched the dead whale with the toe of his boot.

"This one probably caught a .38-caliber bullet in the head. May have died from it anyway, but our catching him made it a sure thing. The shock of the wound and then the shock of being caught on top of that was just too much. It died."

Marlin nodded. He, too, could sympathize with the squid fishermen and the problems that these whales caused them, but he deplored the fact that they would just shoot them at random in such manner. Again, as in so many cases of wildlife destruction, it was something that boiled down to a matter of

money. Where money was concerned, it seemed, all other considerations went out the window.

Behind them now the bulk of Santa Catalina Island was growing dim in the haze, and he asked Boots where they were heading.

"Out just a little farther," Boots replied. "We'll have to drop this whale overboard, but we want to get plenty far away from the pod when we do so. Look back there." He pointed.

Just visible in the distance behind them was the pod of pilot whales, still rising periodically, but much closer to the boat was the mother whale. The whole pod had apparently followed the boat a considerable distance before stopping, but the mother much farther than the rest.

"Ever any danger of the rest of the pod attacking the boat when you take one aboard?" Marlin asked.

It was Brocato who shrugged his shoulders and answered. "Don't know for sure, but we *hope* not!"

They all laughed and the older captain continued: "No, it doesn't seem too likely. Mostly they seem to follow to try to help. Now if we had harpooned it, that might be another matter. The Indians of Nova Scotia used to shoot small harbor porpoises for meat, blubber oil, and head oil, but they left the pilot whales alone. They were very much afraid that the others of the pod would ram them in retaliation. I do recall once hearing, though, that a big bull pilot whale rammed a fifty-foot collecting boat as if he was trying to defend his pod."

Boots now indicated the large female. "She followed right beneath the boat for a long while," he said, "but now she's heading back to the pod. She knows we took her young one aboard, and if we stayed in that area she'd have followed us all day. And if we'd have dropped this dead one back into the water near her, you'd have seen something pretty pathetic."

He went on to tell Marlin how, several years before, they had caught a young whale suffering from some disease, which is something rather common among whales. That one, too, had died and they had dropped it back into the water. A dead whale sinks and so the carcass was quickly lost to sight, but only a minute or so later the young one's mother burst from the surface with the baby in her mouth, desperately trying to get it to breathe. Time after time she had jumped with it, all the while a strange wailing cry coming from her. Hours later, when they had left the area, she was still regularly bringing the baby to the surface to breathe.

"Worse yet," Boots went on, "it doesn't just end there. One time when we were out here we saw a big female pilot whale doing the same thing with a young one in her mouth and got close enough to see better. The baby was beginning to decompose badly and it was obvious that it had been dead for a week or more. Yet here she was, still regularly bringing it to the surface."

"Pretty much the same thing happened in the Marineland tanks," Brocato put it. "Often these pilot whales will form substitute companionships with other species. When Bimbo finally got adapted to life in the tank there, he became very closely attached to a little female striped dolphin named Debbie. They were just about inseparable. Then one day Debbie suddenly died and it was amazing the way Bimbo reacted. First he carried her to the surface and held her there so she could breathe. When she didn't, he took her to the bottom of the tank and guarded her from the divers who were sent in to bring her body out. That was the time we mentioned earlier when Bimbo stayed submerged for ten minutes. In fact, he became very threatening to the divers that time when they came too close, and moved away from them, carrying the carcass by holding one of Debbie's flippers in his mouth. Took us a long while to get her away from him."

They lapsed into silence for a little while and then Boots looked at Marlin and said: "You know, I don't think we have even begun to realize just how intelligent whales are and what strong family and friendship ties they form. We do know that this closeness between mother and young shows itself in the way

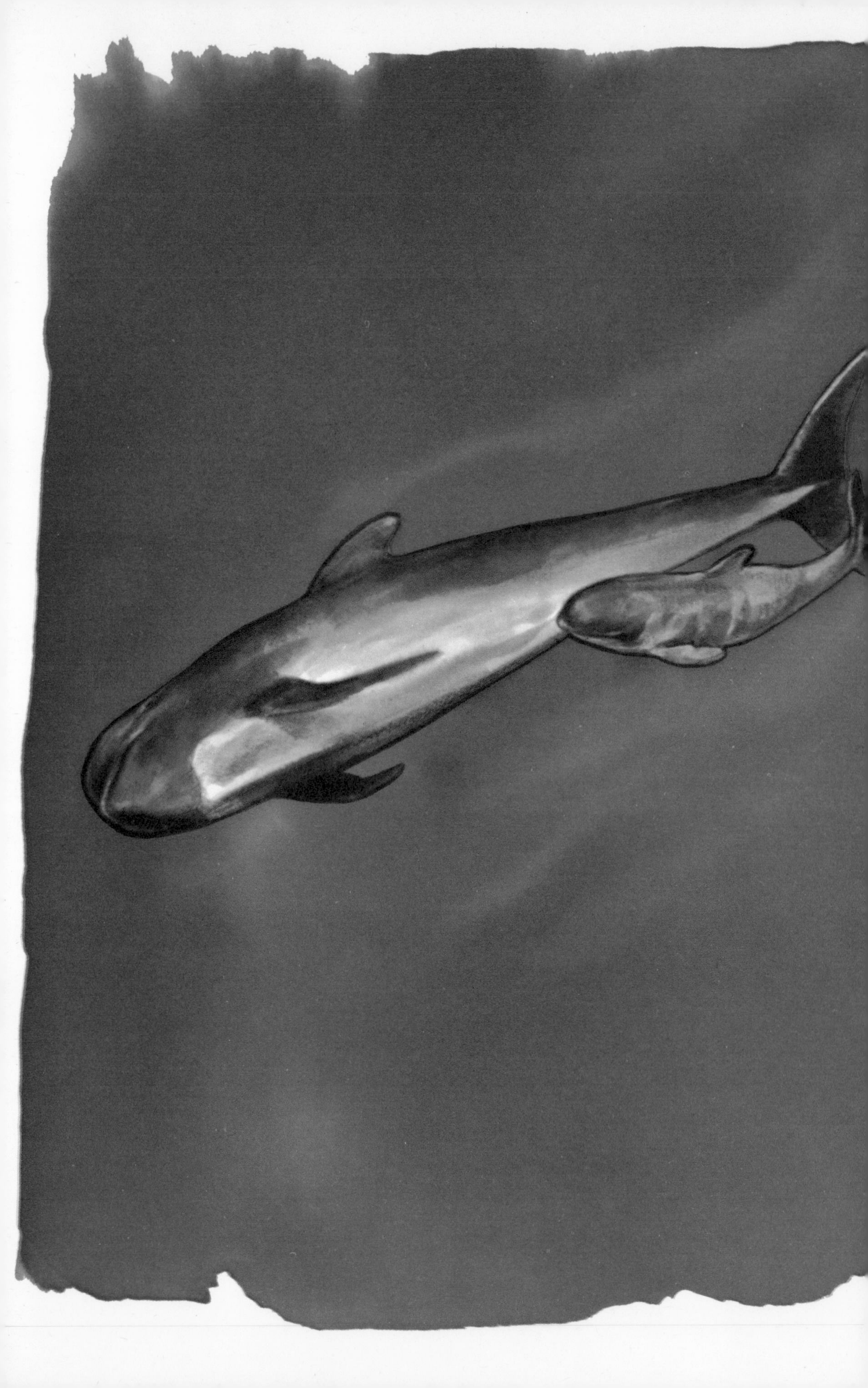

they are reluctant to wean. A calf pilot whale begins to take solid food at from six to nine months of age, but it often continues to nurse from its mother until it is almost two years old and maybe eleven feet long. Seems as if neither the mother nor the young wants to break this close tie that binds them.

"Nor," he added, "do we dare to take a completely nursing calf from its mother or a mother from its calf. Almost without fail, both will die. It's as if they just grieve themselves to death, giving up the will to live because of the separation."

Boots now turned away and went back to the dead whale to measure it and take down some pertinent data. This information he would turn over to the research scientists at Marineland and perhaps it would help to add some few grains of information to man's growing understanding of the nature of whales.

When he finished, Santa Catalina Island was almost out of sight and the whale pod behind them could no longer be seen. Brocato eased the throttle to low and disengaged the gears. Then Benny, Boots, and Marlin worked together to raise the dead whale to the rail, then tip the stretcher to roll it off into the sea.

It was, Marlin thought, strangely like the burial at sea of a person. They all felt a sense of loss. The carcass disappeared in a great splash and the *Geronimo* roared back to life and headed in a great curve toward the island again.

For a long while after that, though, the four on board were oddly subdued and silent, each man lost in his own thoughts.

Chapter Nine

The eighth day passed and the ninth, then the tenth and eleventh. Still the whales managed to elude them. On one of the days the *Geronimo* was suddenly in the midst of a school of tens of thousands of blacksmith fish, and on another day a curious harbor seal paced them only twenty or thirty yards away, its head lifted high and cocked to one side. It was comically as if the animal were trying to determine what these strange-looking creatures were aboard the boat.

Three times in those four days they had found large pods and got within range of them. Once, after Captain Brocato had maneuvered the boat's bowsprit basket right over them, Boots had waved him off.

"Diseased," he called.

The older man had nodded and turned away at once.

"That whole pod was full of carbuncles," Boots said when he returned to the deck. "Big white ones all over them. Every animal had 'em and"—he spoke now to Marlin—"we can't chance taking one like that for fear it would spread disease to all the rest of the captive animals at Marineland. That's something we have to be very careful about." He then went on to explain to Marlin that though he called these sores carbuncles, his use of that term was very general and that actually the causes of the skin ailments afflicting these whales are as yet unknown.

"We've encountered whales with all sorts of afflictions," he continued. "What we call warts and carbuncles—though that may not be what they really are—seem to be the most common disorders, but often a whole pod will be suffering from a severe eczema and sometimes a bad form of pneumonia."

On the other two occasions when they found large pods, Boots had been unsuccessful in casting his noose-net. One time the animal veered just as the cast was made and the weights ineffectively hit the whale. The animal squealed an alarm and within seconds there was not a whale to be seen.

The second cast, early the next day, was nicely made and the net landed properly. It was very early in the morning and the whale was a big bull, easily nineteen feet in length. But this was a smart animal which reacted differently than usual. Instead of surging forward and enabling Boots to tighten the noose over him, he seemed almost to slam brakes on and back off. The noose slid harmlessly off his smoothly rounded head before Boots could yank it tight. Once again the whales took alarm at the signal given by this large male and the pod disappeared.

After that, to while away the long hours of staring at the sea, the men fell to talking. Marlin asked a question that had been nagging him. "What's the normal life span for one of these pilot whales, Frank?"

Brocato shrugged. "Hard to say with any degree of authenticity. We just don't know enough about them yet. About the best way found to tell, though, is by taking a tooth from one that had died, slicing it into thin sections, and then counting the annual rings in it, just as you might in a section of log.

"They don't have many teeth, really—nothing like the killer whale or even the false killers. They have a total of twenty-four to thirty teeth visible through the gums and ten or twelve pairs on each jaw that are rudimentary and buried out of sight in the gums. Compare that to the striped dolphin, which has as many as a hundred twenty-four teeth in both jaws. Another thing, the pilot whale's teeth aren't so much fanglike as the killer whale's. They're more like sharpened pegs and they're pretty far apart from one another.

"Anyway, they've sectioned the teeth and found one female to be fifty years old. The oldest male was forty. We hear a lot of stories about whales getting to be a hundred years old, but that's all those reports are—just stories."

Though Marlin had thoroughly toured the Marineland of the Pacific facility, he was particularly interested in hearing more about how these marine mammals and the oceanarium's many fish were cared for.

Newly captured whales, Boots and Frank told him, were raised by heavy cranelike tackle at the Marineland dock and put aboard trucks. They were driven immediately to the Marineland laboratories where Curator John Prescott and other staff personnel swiftly ran a series of checks and precautionary steps. The whales are accurately measured, weighed, and injected with several antibiotics, not only to prevent them from possibly getting infected from rope burns or possible nicks in the skin they may have suffered during capture, but equally to prevent them from pos-

sibly passing on some sickness to the animals already here.

Then the new whale is taken to an isolation tank into which it is carefully lowered. Normally, even though the animal may have been out of the water for ten or twelve hours or even longer, it is not affected by it. Nevertheless, a diver stands ready for the first several hours to assist any whale, should it sicken or otherwise need help.

In a week or two, having become accustomed to the new life, the whales are introduced to the huge whale tank where they begin their training, not only for entertainment of the public, but for research reasons. In their day by day contact with the whales, dolphins, and fish, the curator and his staff have gained ability and knowledge in the matters of keeping their charges well and happy. At the same time they have added significantly to man's over-all knowledge of marine life.

Almost any marine animal that becomes ill will stop eating. In most cases it is the first tangible sign something is wrong. At night, when no visitors are around to disturb or excite the animals, the ailing creature is given a shot of penicillin and his skin is checked for bumps or infections. While this is happening, the other whales or dolphins lie quietly in the water, seeming to sense that the men are there to help, not hurt. Often, if nothing external can be found wrong, an extra vitamin capsule is inserted into a small fish and then fed to the ailing animal.

It is more difficult to treat fish, as they cannot be so easily isolated as the marine mammals. The larger and more valuable

specimens are closely watched and care is taken to help them in any way possible. And when, as must happen from time to time, a specimen dies of sickness or old age, a post-mortem examination and autopsy is performed in the laboratory. Even in this way a great deal of valuable information has been gained—information which cannot help but preserve the lives of other inhabitants of Marineland.

Talking about such matters as these helped considerably to keep time from hanging too heavily on the men of the *Geronimo* during these last four days. Nevertheless, the same thought was constantly in the minds of all of them: would they get another chance at a whale or would they ultimately have to return empty-handed?

And now, at last, on this twelfth day out, the *Geronimo* was approaching the largest pod they had yet encountered on this expedition. Not only were there easily sixty or seventy whales in it, but within sight were two other pods which seemed almost as large. Even better, it was early morning and if the opportunity presented itself, they could take one of the large ones.

Carefully Brocato eased back on the throttle as they neared the animals and Boots took his place on the wildly pitching bowsprit. Though the wind was a little heavier than it had been in previous days, it still wasn't bad. Where the swells were concerned, it was an entirely different matter. They were huge and when the *Geronimo* was heading into them, the bowsprit basket rose and fell a great distance. Sometimes the bowsprit pointed upward at as much of an angle as forty degrees and at other times it plunged so deeply beneath the water surface that Boots was covered to his waist and he had to hang onto the basket rail with all his strength to keep from being torn away.

As such, it was not an ideal day for whale-catching purposes, but there was nothing to do but go ahead and make the effort. With the pilot whales so suddenly abundant, luck might run with the men on this attempt. And, for a while at least, it seemed that such would be the case.

Frank Brocato throttled down to about four knots, which was roughly the speed these whales were traveling and his gaze locked on the large whale singled out by Boots, who was pointing at it. About eighteen or nineteen feet in length, the whale was a fine bull with a great globular head and a seeming disdain for the boat approaching from behind.

The mammal maintained a steady speed of three or four knots just fifteen feet ahead of the bowsprit, coming up regularly to breathe, as did the rest of the pod. And with this many whales all around them blowing at the same time, there was abruptly a great stench in the air and Brocato grinned.

"Healthy whales," he told Marlin. "Seems as if the healthier they are, the worse their breath smells. Sometimes it gets pretty bad. Good thing we've got a little breeze today. I've seen it make some people violently sick. Good thing for the whales, too, that they don't have a sense of smell. Otherwise they couldn't stand each other's company."

Marlin smiled halfheartedly. He could certainly understand why. He gritted his teeth and determined that he wasn't going to let it get him. He breathed shallowly through his mouth and concentrated on the activity taking place and in that way the awful halitosis didn't bother him too badly.

For perhaps an eighth of a mile they followed the bull while the animal maintained his distance from the *Geronimo*. Then, as the whale breathed and submerged again to continue swimming along eight or ten feet below the surface, Boots nodded and Brocato pushed the throttle up a little. Gradually, ever so gradually, the *Geronimo* overtook the whale. For a moment it looked as if their luck would hold and they'd get him.

Then everything changed in an instant. Abruptly the whale slowed and began to rise rapidly. Boots flung out a hand to warn Brocato and Brocato, who had also seen the whale's action, jerked the throttle back to the idle, but it was too late. An unusually large swell caught the boat, drawing the stern far down in a trough and raising the bowsprit basket until Boots was

higher than Marlin, who was on the mast straddling the lookout perch.

The swell passed, the balance shifted, and the bowsprit plunged downward sharply, smacking into the water and dunking Boots all the way to his neck. With even greater bad luck, the bowsprit planking smacked solidly onto the back of the whale.

Boots very nearly catapulted out of the basket and dropped the noose-net as he strove to hang on against the pressure of the water and rolling of the boat. The whale was not hurt, but he was most definitely startled. Even though still under the water, the animal made a sound everyone aboard could hear clearly and then itself shot downward into the depths of the ocean.

Within seconds all of the whales of this entire pod were gone, having sounded deeply. Now it was obvious that they were badly frightened. It would undoubtedly be many minutes before they surfaced again and they would probably not again allow the *Geronimo* to get so close to them.

Soaked and shaken, Boots made his way carefully back to the boat and shook his head ruefully. "Tough luck," he said, "but could've been a lot worse."

Brocato nodded seriously and explained to Marlin, who by this time had climbed down from the mast to join him.

"Boots is right," he said. "It can be very dangerous when the bowsprit goes into the water. If it goes down far enough and the boat begins to right itself quickly enough, there's a good chance the bowsprit planking will snap. If that happens it's big trouble. All those cables," he said, pointing to the heavy wires leading from bowsprit to boat, "are under great tension. If the planking snapped, they'd throw the bowsprit and basket—and Boots, too! —back toward the boat. Be apt to kill Boots or whoever's in the basket, and anyone else back here, too, that the cables might hit."

Since one of the main bowsprit cables was attached to the mast right where Marlin had been perched and there would have been no possibility of him ducking out of the way, Marlin could well see how dangerous a situation it had been. He made a mental note that hereafter when the swells were running heavily, he would remain on deck.

Recovered somewhat in these few minutes, Boots pointed landward and spoke to Brocato: "Still one group over there that wasn't scared off, Frank. Head for them while I get the noose back in shape." Already he was pulling in the noose-net which, held by the tie lines, had been dragging beneath the boat.

Marlin, accustomed to facing danger in many ways, marveled at the fact that despite the close call Boots had had and his accompanying drenching, the skipper was already edging out on the bowsprit again with the noose-net. It was, Marlin decided, an act that took considerable courage.

The pod of whales they were now heading for was closer to the shore of Catalina Island and they were continuing their normal surfacing maneuvers, apparently undisturbed by the activity that had taken place almost two miles from them which had sent the other pod deep below the surface. They took no particular notice of the *Geronimo* as it approached them.

The whales of the frightened pod had by this time resurfaced several thousand yards behind the boat and were headed in the other direction. Abruptly, however, they paused and began milling. Several of the larger bulls came a considerable way out of the water, looking back toward the *Geronimo* rapidly approaching the other pod. Three of these whales then plunged into headlong speed right on the surface—not away from the boat, but directly at it!

Ten or twelve others followed them immediately and this group of whales now charged through the water at such speed that they left great foaming swirls behind them as they greyhounded along the surface. For a rather frightening moment it appeared that they were bent on ramming the *Geronimo*, and the four men aboard felt their muscles tense and their grips on rails or rigging tighten automatically.

Then it became evident that they were not the target of the approach. The whales were evidently coming to join the other pod, apparently to warn them or lead them to safety. Though the *Geronimo* was traveling at about nine knots, the cluster of whales sped past the boat a hundred yards away as if the craft were standing still. They reached the milling whales ahead long before the boat got there.

For a minute or so the newly arrived whales moved rapidly back and forth about the large pod, often breaking surface sharply. And then, as if orders had been given and the commands followed, the entire pod formed itself into a long line stretching two or three hundred yards and, moving rapidly and

surfacing every minute or so to breathe, headed away from the *Geronimo.*

The men aboard ship watched the entire episode with keen interest. There could be no doubt that communication of some kind had taken place among the whales. And even though it was obviously to their own disadvantage, the men were grateful that they had been able to witness a phenomenon of nature not yet well understood by man.

"As I said before," Boots commented wryly, "we haven't even begun to understand yet how smart they are and how much they actually try to help each other. The way they're leaving now, you'd think they'll be staying together, but they won't. As soon as the pod is out of danger, those bulls will rejoin their own pod and go their own way.

"The pods are almost like clans," he continued. "Each whale knows just where he belongs. Sometimes they'll mix together, but as soon as it's time to go, they'll all assemble in their own proper groups and go their own ways. More than once I've seen them help each other out of possible dangers like that. Maybe someday we'll learn more about how they communicate and how their family groups are set up and maintained. It's really a rather complex system and that in itself denotes a rather high degree of intelligence. Anyway," he concluded, "we may as well give up for the day. As badly as they're all stirred up now, we're not apt to do any good."

Chapter Ten

By the afternoon of the thirteenth day afloat, it began to seem that the expedition was going to prove a failure insofar as whales were concerned. Not because of a failure to find whales—they had found many pods of them—but because the whales themselves seemed to have become extraordinarily skittish and it was most difficult to approach very closely without the pods becoming alarmed and sounding.

Northern striped dolphins frequently came leaping toward the *Geronimo* and then amused themselves by "running" with the bow wave, often turning on their sides or backs to look up at the boat and at the men looking down at them.

Marlin mused on the difference between dolphins and porpoises—a difference so often confusing to people, including even many scientists themselves, mainly because the terms are pretty loosely used.

The classical dolphin—*Delphinus delphis*—is a small whalelike mammal with a beaked snout, white chest, and faint dark bands down its sides. Though it is a creature which does not usually adapt well to captivity, Marineland presently has three such animals trained and living in the same tank with the killer whale.

These northern striped dolphin now pacing the *Geronimo*, however, normally do extremely well in captivity and seem to enjoy it, adapting well. Known by the scientific name of *Lagenorhynchus obliquidens*, they are commonly called *Lag* for short. This is a dolphin with a very short snout-beak. And because of a gray area on the dorsal fin, which looks white underwater and shows up clearly, many people call the animal spotfin.

The most highly trained and presumably most intelligent dolphins are those known by the scientific name of *Tursiops*. The Pacific Ocean species is *Tursiops gilli*, while the slightly different Atlantic species is *Tursiops truncatus*. They, too, have a relatively short beak but they don't have the sharply defined color pattern that *Lag* shows. *Tursiops* is most commonly known by the name of bottlenose dolphin or, incorrectly, bottlenose porpoise.

The Americans, Marlin was aware, use the name porpoise more than the English, who use it mainly to mean the small whalelike mammals that have no beak. This, in essence, classifies the pilot whales, false killer whales, and killer whales as large porpoises.

Of course it further complicates the picture, Marlin reflected, when one considers that there is also a true fish called the dolphin. It is a warm-water game fish common in tropical or semitropical oceans throughout the world. Called *mahi-mahi* in Hawaii, its scientific name is *Coryphaena hippurus*.

But while the *Lags* and *Tursiops* occasionally cavorting about the bow of the boat were interesting to watch, they weren't pilot whales, the expedition's objective. Nor did it help to have *Tursiops* around because when whale pods were neared, the dolphin would spurt ahead to join them and the pod would take alarm and sound at once, as if the dolphin had warned them.

Time after time this thirteenth morning—whether or not the

dolphins were around—they had tried to approach pods, only to have the whales suddenly begin collecting and then heading rapidly away in long lines which sometimes spanned a thousand yards or more.

They did see something, however, which Marlin found most interesting, and he was very glad they had not missed it. A pod of adult whales about a mile and a half distant suddenly began breaching—that is, flinging themselves entirely clear of the water and then crashing back to the surface with splashes so loud that even they, on the boat, could hear them.

"Now and then they'll do it," Brocato said, "but we don't exactly know why. Maybe they're feeding on something different and they do that to confuse their quarry; maybe they're just playing. It's another of those things we just don't know enough about whales to identify for sure yet. One thing, though, it's an impressive sight."

Impressive it was. The whale would apparently rise at high speed from far below the surface and burst into the air in a leap which would take him as much as six or seven feet clear of the water. He would then half turn in mid-air and fall back on his side with that tremendous splash and thereby create a huge wave and a great white swirl of foam.

But though the *Geronimo* headed immediately for the breaching pod, the story was the same; as soon as the scattered whales detected the boat's approach, they drew together, formed their "traveling" line, and set off at good speed in the opposite direction. It was fruitless to attempt taking one when they were traveling in this manner.

Once again the *Geronimo* began moving eastward along the south shore of Santa Catalina Island. About midway between Catalina Harbor, where they had been mooring most nights, and the town of Avalon at the eastern end of the island, there are a couple of relatively level shore lines made up principally of rocks well rounded by water action. These areas were the resting places of some of the great herds of harbor seals and sea lions of the area.

Now, as they neared these places, Marlin studied the shore line with binoculars. Frank Brocato had told him that with supplies growing short, tomorrow would have to be their last day of whale hunting. If they hadn't nabbed their whale by noon, they'd have to call it quits. And now since it seemed apparent that whale hunting was going to prove fruitless today, Marlin asked Frank Brocato about the plan of possibly collecting one of the sea lions for Marineland.

Brocato agreed that it was as good a time as any for getting one. Marineland needed another good specimen and chances were good that with the animals basking as they were, they might be able to net one. Since all they had so far to take home was the blue shark, this would at least help ease the disappointment of not getting a whale.

There were perhaps eighty of the animals on shore and another dozen or so swimming about in the great swells which pounded ashore here. Those basking were thirty or forty yards from the water and so, if they landed their skiff out of sight of them and approached unseen on shore, they might be able to rush from cover and net one. The four men planned their strategy carefully while Boots and Marlin rigged up a strong net.

The winch was used to lower the *Geronimo*'s skiff into the water and Marlin got in first. He was followed by Boots, who would man the oars and get them safely ashore. At best, it would be a tricky and possibly dangerous landing. Benny and Frank stayed aboard the *Geronimo* as the skiff headed toward shore. Almost immediately, however, the sea lions began to show nervousness.

By twos and threes they waddled to the water and plunged in, then milled about curiously near the shore. The closer the skiff approached, even though it was not headed directly at them, the more sea lions slipped away.

Graceful, streamlined, and amazingly agile in the water, the animals could easily outmaneuver any attempts to catch them in their watery element. If the men could surprise some still on

shore, however, the seals would be at a disadvantage. Ashore, the animal is awkward and not too fast.

Now the inshore undertow was gripping the boat and Boots had his hands full maneuvering for the landing. No matter how they did it, bucking these swells among the rocks was deadly business. If for just an instant the boat got out of control, it could be smashed to splinters the next moment.

Boots watched the incoming swells and timed his movements just exactly right to catch one perfectly. The swell lifted the boat and helped shoot it bowfirst into the tiny cove. Just before they disappeared behind the last big jutting rocks from where the herd had been sunning, Marlin saw that only a scattered few of the animals now remained on shore. Their only hope would be to cut off a straggler.

The boat grated harshly ashore on the rocks and in the same instant Boots and Marlin leaped out and dragged it high enough on shore that it would not be pulled back out by the waves. With Boots carrying the net, the pair ran as fast as they could

on the rocky ground and rounded the last boulder in time to see that just one sea lion remained far up on shore.

The animal saw them at the same time and he broke into a scrambling run which, despite its awkwardness, covered much ground rapidly. Boots and the sea lion reached the same spot on the shore line at almost the same moment and with a diving thrust, Boots managed to get the heavy net over the animal. In an instant Marlin was beside him, helping to hold the frantic animal and drag it back from the water's edge.

It wasn't easy. The sea lion was a young bull weighing in the neighborhood of three hundred pounds. It was every bit as determined to get into the water as the men were to keep it out. For a little while it looked as if the seal would win. Boots skidded on the slick rocks and his feet went out from under him. Marlin, thrown off balance, tumbled atop him. Nevertheless, they managed to hold onto the netting and struggle back to their feet, drenched by a wave that had pounded in and was more of a help to the sea lion than to them.

Little by little they pulled the struggling animal far up on the

rocks, but even then it continued to fight to get free. They rebraced themselves, got fresh firm grips on the webbing of the net, and then began hauling their frightened quarry toward the skiff. It was a big job.

Fortunately for them both, the sea lion had about worn itself out by the time they reached the little craft. It was something of a difficulty boosting the animal over the gunwale into the boat and then shoving off, but they made it at last. Marlin just about straddled the sea lion to hold it still while Boots rowed for all he was worth.

Aboard the *Geronimo*, Benny had readied the cage below deck in the aft hold and by the time the small boat got there, he was ready with the winch and boom. A strong line was attached to the net and the animal was lifted smoothly by the boom into the larger boat and down into the hatch to the waiting cage. There was a momentary problem as the sea lion, barking hoarsely, made another frantic effort to get free, but then he was out of the netting and into the cage and Benny and Boots closed and sealed the cage. The job was over.

At the cost of skinned knees, elbows, knuckles, and almost utter exhaustion on the parts of Boots and Marlin, they had their sea lion. Marlin suspected—and rightly so—that he and Boots would have some pretty stiff and sore muscles for the next few days to come.

Once more the *Geronimo* headed for its nightly anchorage at the center of the island. As they moved smoothly over the swells, Marlin thought of all they had done these past two weeks. He accepted with thanks the steaming cup of coffee Benny handed him and sipped with pleasure at it.

Tomorrow would be the last half day of whale hunting, and Marlin knew there was no sense in deluding themselves with the idea that they were going to catch one. If they hadn't been able to get their live quarry in thirteen days, another half day was not apt to prove profitable. Yet, though they might not take home a whale, the trip was far from a failure. Expeditions very often had a tendency not to turn out exactly as planned, but rarely could any of them be termed failures. The many things already seen and done had made this venture a success.

While he had spent a lifetime among animals and in a wide variety of habitats of the wild kingdom, each expedition was a new thrill and a great adventure. And each time, without exception, he saw and learned things previously unknown to him. Such was the case with this expedition. Yes, the capture of a live whale would have been the icing to the cake, but the cake was still there and they had all benefited from it.

And anyway, he thought, who knows—there's always tomorrow.

Chapter Eleven

It was the morning of the fourteenth day at sea and in a few hours they would be heading in—returning to Marineland of the Pacific with their blue shark and sea lion, but without their prime objective, a pilot whale.

Nevertheless, for Marlin it had been an exciting journey into a watery realm, a wild kingdom of the sea, and he would come away with a whole new crop of memories and considerable new information. And even for the crew of the *Geronimo*, who were far more familiar with this type of expedition than he, the trip had been a stimulating one and well worth the effort.

As they cruised along the southwestern coast of the island they talked about the expedition: the sights they had seen, the sounds they had heard, the things they had experienced. They talked about the young whale that had been shot and then died when captured, and that gave Marlin pause to ask a question that had been puzzling him.

"What," he said, directing his question at both Brocato and Calandrino, "have you found out about courtship and reproduction among the pilot whales?"

The two captains looked at one another and at a faint dip of Brocato's head, Boots was the one who replied.

"Not a great deal," he admitted. "A certain degree of courtship has occurred in the tanks between Bubbles and Bimbo, but about all this amounted to was some head butting. Bimbo would smack Bubbles with a blow that would shake both their bodies and force Bubbles backward a few feet, since she was the smaller of the two. Then they'd swim around side by side for a while. Gradually Bubbles would pull ahead of him a few feet and then smack him alongside the head with her flukes. They've never really seriously tried to mate, though."

"We *do* know," Brocato put in as Boots paused, "that they're very slow breeders. It takes from fourteen to sixteen months after breeding for the baby to be born, then another six to nine months of the baby feeding on mother's milk alone, followed by another thirteen to sixteen months of the baby both nursing and feeding on solids. That makes it a good three or four years between single births for each cow. Double fetuses have been found inside some cows that were harpooned, and

Boots and I have seen what appears to be twins following a single cow, but we have no definite proof that there has ever been more than one baby whale born at one time."

The *Geronimo* had now come to West End, the outer tip of Santa Catalina Island. Off their starboard beam was the great jutting pinnacle known as Eagle Rock, which projected eight or ten stories high straight out of the water like a gigantic spear point. Now Frank Brocato spun the wheel to curve around West End and head the boat due east and back to the mainland.

Marlin watched the curiously white-topped Eagle Rock for a few minutes and then turned to Brocato to ask him a question. It never came out because just then Benny gave a sharp cry.

"Animals!"

Instantly an electric excitement gripped all of them and they turned their gaze to follow the direction of the deck hand's point. Not far from the sharply cliffed shore line, a pod of perhaps a dozen pilot whales was rising in haphazard manner, obviously engaged in feeding. Brocato spun the wheel even more and the boat headed in their direction.

There were six or seven adults in the pod and four calves. Three of these young ones were much too small—obviously animals still not weaned. But one of them was a fine young whale of perhaps eight feet in length. It mostly swam beside one of the large females, but occasionally moved off by itself some distance to hunt. It was on this one that the gaze of Brocato at the controls and Boots in the basket now locked.

With the clouds high and thin and the water very blue and clear, the whales were not unduly alarmed by the approach of the boat. Within five minutes or so the *Geronimo* was among them, throttled down to about two or three knots and gently following the young eight-footer which had now taken a position beside its mother again.

Not unexpectedly, just as the *Geronimo*'s bowsprit basket got over them, the whales sounded, disappearing quickly into the depths. Four sets of eyes scanned the water intently, awaiting their return. It was Marlin who saw them surface this time, at an angle behind the boat.

"There!" he cried, pointing.

Brocato swung the boat around and in another few minutes

another approach was made. Once again the whales sounded and once again they watched and waited, slowly circling. Again it was Marlin who was looking at the right spot when they surfaced again fifty yards away.

For the third time the *Geronimo* got into position behind them, and it was obvious that this would probably be their last chance. The pod had drawn together now, becoming just a bit alarmed at this craft which dogged their every move. They formed into a straight line and began heading out to sea, surfacing to breathe every minute or so and traveling only five or six feet below the surface.

Slowly and carefully, using Boots's pointing arm as a guide, Brocato followed the animals and gradually increased his speed. Boots tensed and leaned far over the basket rim. The whales were almost directly below him now, just a little bit ahead. The young one and its mother began to rise, but it was the young one whose head broke the surface first. It turned slightly on its side, saw the man in the basket directly above for the first time, and suddenly panicked, veering sharply and thrusting away at an angle to the left of Boots.

The seaman launched his noose-net in a desperate thrust. It was much too far a shot for accuracy and by all rights it should have been a miss . . . but it wasn't.

As if it had eyes of its own, the noose-net settled perfectly over the whale's head and even before it could fully react, Boots had jerked the noose tight. The fight was on. Once again the line ripped away from the boat and then began whirring out of the box in a veritable blur. In moments Benny had the line wrapped around both the pulley block and winch drum and Brocato was gradually easing the *Geronimo* away from the sheer cliffs and farther out into open waters.

Though this whale was smaller than the one roped before, it was much more energetic and determined not to be brought in. Back and forth it sped about far below the surface, causing the rope to hiss through the water. Down it went, nearly two hundred feet, then up again to burst from the water in a great splash.

Two, three, four times more it broke water before sounding again, but this time it went down only fifty feet or so before the pressure of the winch slowed and stopped it and then gradually began drawing it toward the boat.

"Didn't go too far down, Frank," Benny called to Boots. "Lots of line left."

Boots, already coming back to the deck, nodded. "Not like that one that went down twelve hundred feet, eh Benny?" He grinned at Marlin and added: "They don't usually sound much deeper than this one. Even when they're hunting they normally don't go down much more than a hundred feet. After that the visibility gets too poor and they have to waste too much time hunting for their quarry."

All this while the winch was slowly turning and Brocato had come down to give a hand. He was now guiding the line so it would not foul as it came off the winch spool. The other whales were milling about in a frightened manner and as the young whale was brought closer to the boat, the air was filled with sharp squalls and whistling cries. Time and again the mother endeavored to knock the rope off her young one . . . and then she partially succeeded!

"Frank, the rope!" Boots yelled. "She must've knocked it loose enough for it to slide over the dorsal. It's tightened up again behind the fin but it may not stay. We'll have to take it easy on this one."

As the baby whale was brought to the starboard side of the boat, the mother whale continued to remain very close by—perhaps five feet under the surface and no more than six feet away. Once she turned on her back and tried to grasp the rope in her teeth, but she failed. The rope did, however, momentarily catch around her fluke and she carried it under the boat before pulling herself free.

The *Geronimo* crew had performed perfectly as a team, each man doing his own particular job at just the right time. In a matter of moments the young whale had been brought gently to the side of the boat. Now it could be seen that if the little mam-

mal chose to begin struggling again, the noose might easily slip away and so, with careful haste another noose was positioned around the tail and tightened and another loop around the front portion of the body.

Now, however, it became apparent that there was another problem, and a serious one at that. The length of rope the mother whale had pulled beneath the boat and then freed herself of had apparently become tightly fouled around something. No amount of pulling or jerking could get it off and as long as it was fouled like that, the canvas stretcher could not be lowered over and around the captive whale.

Almost always in the catching of whales in this manner there is a certain amount of minor bleeding. Mostly this comes when the second noose is drawn tightly around the tail just in front of the flukes, for there the skin seems to be surprisingly tender. This is not serious bleeding, but it *is* blood in the water and blood brings sharks. It became obvious now that, with this little whale bleeding from the rope burn at the tail as well as slightly from where the rope had been yanked by the mother across the dorsal fin, sharks would very soon be attracted. If they couldn't get that rope free in short order, the little whale would almost certainly be attacked.

Until now Marlin had been more or less a spectator to the capturing of the whale, his chief contribution being that of keeping out of the way while the experienced whalers did their work. But now, assessing the situation at a glance, he raced into the cabin and jerked his clothing off, then quickly donned the heavy rubber wet-suit. He strapped the scuba outfit around him, swiftly tested it, adjusted the mask, and then raced to the rail. Biting hard on the mouthpiece and holding the mask in place, he jumped feet first off the rail of the *Geronimo* into the sea beside the captive whale.

Brocato, too, had surged into action. At once he stopped the motor and from a locker inside the cabin he removed a heavy .370-magnum big-game rifle. He thrust one shell into the chamber and two more of the cartridges into the magazine. Then, he, too, raced back to the rail to stand watch.

Both tail and dorsal fin of the little whale were now bleeding a bit more freely and faint ribbons of blood trailed away in the water. The same thought was uppermost in everyone's mind: sharks. If there were any nearby—and there was every reason to believe there were—they would be showing up very soon. They would not hesitate to attack either the pinioned whale or Marlin Perkins.

Marlin, in the meanwhile, swam beneath the surface to the outside of the whale. Below him and fifteen or twenty feet away he could see the mother hovering and he breathed a silent prayer that she would remain where she was and not charge him. One pile-driving ramming of that great head against him, backed up by more than a ton of body weight, would mean the end for him.

Fortunately the whale stayed where she was and Marlin concentrated on the rope. It was immediately obvious that he

would be able to do nothing about freeing it from this side of the little whale. He would have to get on the other side, between whale and boat, but below both. Gingerly he swam down and passed beneath the huge tail, hoping the men above would retain a good grip on the rope. One smashing blow from that tail could break his bones.

The tail remained firmly held, though now Marlin could clearly see the blood stream trailing away from it. The swells caused a powerful backwash under the boat as it lifted and fell and for an instant, Marlin was almost sucked in between the captive whale and the side of the boat. An instant later that gap closed again as the whale thumped solidly against the hull. A man caught between would have been crushed.

Marlin looked about carefully, tracing the route of the rope. There! The rope that was fouled was caught on a rough projection on the keel. It wouldn't take too much effort to get it off, he thought, but it would take a little time and right now time was extremely important. Even as he swam to free the rope, Marlin could see coming toward him from the distance and below, no less than five blue sharks.

The full blood lust had still not risen in these fish. The blood trail was faint and they were merely investigating, not knowing what they might find. But even as they came closer and the scent became stronger in the water, Marlin could see them becoming excited. The sharks increased their speed and two of them shot past below him and the whale.

Now more of them were coming. They were all around and below the boat, perhaps a dozen or more of them. A vague caution still seemed to ride them, however, at this strange sight in the water. One of them, larger and bolder than the others, moved higher in the water, no more than a foot or so beneath the surface. It seemed to be studying Marlin and then started toward him.

Before it had moved more than a yard, a faint popping sound reached Marlin and a heavy bullet speared through the water and struck the back of the big shark. Instantly it veered away, trailing its own stream of blood and at once a number of the others began following it. But more sharks were coming all the time.

Marlin grasped the rope and tugged hard. It was wedged pretty tightly, more so than he had expected. Again he yanked and this time it came free. Immediately it was pulled tight from above.

Again there came a popping sound from above, but this time Marlin didn't see where the shot went. His own eyes were locked on the rope ladder that had been thrown overboard ahead of the captive whale and he swam for it for all he was worth.

The bottom of the ladder flopped loosely in the water and it was hard to get a footing on it. At last he got one foot positioned and began to lift himself upward. A strong hand suddenly plunged beneath the surface and grabbed his wrist and he felt himself being dragged aboard.

With Benny's help he scrambled over the rail, swinging his feet out of the water just an instant before a shark swept past and turned sideways, jaws agape. It earned for itself not a meaty foot, but a bullet which smashed into its white underside and caused a burst of blood to haze the water.

Already Brocato had set the rifle aside and he and Boots were positioning the stretcher under the whale. In a moment they had it right and were winching it up, out of the water, over the rail and into the boat. In another moment both Marlin and the young whale lay on the deck, exhausted by their efforts.

As if realizing that any further struggling was useless, the young whale lay perfectly still on the deck, its big soft eyes blinking slowly now and then. The large blow-hole opened and closed every twenty or thirty seconds with that sneezelike, explosive breathing.

Marlin had flung off his mask and was himself panting heavily. He could not remember feeling so utterly worn out and realized that it was as much relief from tension as relief from exertion

which made him feel this way. It *had* been a tight situation down there.

Boots had removed the tight noose from the whale's tail and was inspecting the damage. Despite the blood which had flowed from both it and the scrape on the dorsal fin, neither wound was at all severe and both would heal quickly. The large foam-rubber chunks were placed to keep the flippers free from being mashed by the whale's weight, and a bed sheet was draped over the shiny black body. Highly susceptible to sunburn, they must be covered very soon and the sheet constantly wetted down from hose or bucket.

Wearily, Marlin got to his feet and removed his scuba gear and rubber suit. After thoroughly drying himself, he redressed. Within a few minutes he rejoined the crew. The stretcher still around the whale had been raised slightly on sides and end to form a sort of trough in which the whale lay. A pump had been activated and now Benny was holding a hose and the water gushing from it was filling the stretcher trough. This would not only help keep the whale wet, but would provide some buoyancy for the animal.

Marlin reached out and patted the smooth, shiny skin that was so amazingly like the texture of his own rubber scuba-diving suit. The whale's skin was cool to the touch but not cold. Marlin knew the whale's body temperature could not be judged by feeling the skin. Just as the layer of blubber beneath the skin protected the whale from frigid water temperatures, so, too, it kept the body temperature of approximately ninety-six degrees from escaping. Blubber in whales and other marine mammals performs the same insulating function that fur does for land mammals.

Boots now straightened from a brief examination of the animal and grinned widely at Marlin as he pocketed a tape measure.

"A little female," he said, "and she seems to be in perfect health. She's eight feet, two inches long and I'd guess about five hundred pounds."

He reached out and took Marlin's hand and shook it warmly. In his eyes there was a newer and deeper respect as he said, "Good job, Marlin. Good job!"

Within a few minutes the bow of the *Geronimo* was once again pointed toward Palos Verdes Peninsula and Marineland under the able hand of Captain Brocato. Boots turned on the ship-to-shore radio and called the coastal operator. In a few

minutes he had been connected with personnel at Marineland.

"We're coming in," he said. "Will arrive at Marineland dock at approximately 4:30 P.M. Have the boys waiting for us. We're bringing in a blue shark, a sea lion, and a fine young female pilot whale."

The voice answering on the radio was scratchy and harsh but obviously delighted. "Fine! We'll be ready and waiting. Sounds as if you boys had a good trip."

Boots grinned at Brocato, Benny, and Marlin and winked. "Yes," he replied, "a very good trip. Over and out."

Index

R. MARLIN PERKINS, the commentator and star of the weekly television program, "Wild Kingdom," is the director of the world-famous St. Louis Zoological Gardens. His career began at this same St. Louis Zoo, where his first job was as a laborer —sweeping sidewalks and trimming hedges. He rose rapidly to become curator of reptiles, and was then offered the position as curator of the zoo in Buffalo, New York. From Buffalo, he moved to Chicago, where he was director of the Lincoln Park Zoo.

His television career started in Chicago, where he was the star of the program "Zoo Parade." After his return to St. Louis in 1962, when he became director of the zoo, he started "Wild Kingdom," a program that has won countless awards, including the coveted "Emmy."

ALLAN W. ECKERT, the author of IN SEARCH OF A WHALE, has eleven other books to his credit, including *The Great Auk, A Time of Terror, The Silent Sky, Wild Season, The Frontiersmen, Bayou Backwaters* (another "Wild Kingdom" adventure), *The King Snake, The Dreaming Tree, The Crossbreed, Blue Jacket,* and *Wilderness Empire.* Mr. Eckert has also had numerous articles published in a wide variety of magazines, including *The Saturday Evening Post, True, Look, The Reader's Digest, Sports Afield, Field & Stream,* and *Outdoor Life.*

He was born in Buffalo, New York, attended Ohio State University and the University of Dayton, and then began to work as a newspaper reporter. In 1960 he decided to become a full-time writer—a profession that he has followed with increasing success ever since. Mr. Eckert lives in Englewood, Florida, with his wife and two small children.